16

# Reflections
## in the
# Rearview Mirror

# Reflections
# in the
# Rearview Mirror

by

## Jack Warner

dmc books
Dover, NH

Published by
dmc associates, inc.
PO Box 1095
Dover, NH   03821

ISBN: 1-879848-29-5

Printed in the United States of America

First Printing

# Acknowledgments

The late Will McDonough of *The Boston Globe* was a towering figure on the Boston sports scene. He was respected across the entire spectrum of the National Football League for his knowledge and savvy. He was a meticulous writer who always called 'em as he saw 'em. Polly and I have been fortunate to call Will and his wife Denise good friends. They read the first draft of this work. Will's comment was: "There are the makings of a half-dozen good movies in this book." Denise said, "It's terrific, Jack. An awful lot of folks are going to ask you 'Who is Harry?'"
I thank Will and Denise for their encouragement.


Bob Crane has encouraged me in my writing in sunshine and in shadow. Robert Q. Crane was the elected Treasurer of the Commonwealth of Massachusetts for twenty-seven years. He organized and oversaw the establishment of the Massachusetts State Lottery. Anyone who has been blessed with his friendship knows that they have won one of life's most important lotteries.


I want to thank Marie Williams of Watermark in the town of Chatham for her always able and charming assistance in helping assemble this work, and for her skill in creating the dust jacketr.


To those of you who purchase this book, I offer these words which were uttered by my oldest son's father-in-law-to-be when he presented his marvelous daughter to my son at the altar – "Here she is, no deposit, no return."

To Polly – Forevermore

# Reflections
# in the
# Rearview Mirror

# A First Glance

Every summer I join a group of my friends for a noontime baseball game of the Pawtucket Red Sox. This is a group that mostly shares the life experience of having gone to the same college. In our case, Yale. We are not recent graduates.

Not too long ago, on a second of August, we assembled from distant points in New England and New Jersey for our annual day of reminiscence and good fellowship. August 2nd proved to be the hottest day of the summer.

Three friends rode with me from Cape Cod. We arrived early to watch batting practice. As we pulled into the parking area we were amazed at the long lines of buses from all over New England. These buses were full of children. The area outside the ballpark looked like a Little League convention. A fellow walked by and told us the game was sold out. This was numbing news. The creator and organizer of these reunions was driving up from New Jersey and had not arrived yet. He never bought tickets in advance. No one ever expected one of these Paw Sox games to be sold out.

Finally, eight of us were assembled. There was some puzzled discussion on what to do. We were told standing room seats would be sold at game time. The temperature was now in the 90's – a number that some of my friends would be pushing pretty soon — but the hell with it, we decided, we'd go for the standing room tickets.

There were three long lines formed for standing room sales. I got at the end of one with two pals behind me. They each put their hands out and proffered me money. "Here, Jack, take this for the tickets."

"No," I said. And for absolutely no reason, I added, "Put

your money in your pockets. In about fifteen minutes someone will come by and say, 'Hey Jack, how're you doin'? Would you like eight tickets for the game?'"

My friends gave me the old, nodding-head, pursed-lipped, "yeah, sure" look.

After about ten minutes of standing in the baking sun wondering how long our contingent would last standing inside watching the ball game, a young, pleasant faced woman walked up to me. "Do you bank with Citizens Bank?" she asked.

"No." I responded. "Do you work for them?"

"Yes, I do."

"Well," I said, "then I can see why it would make sense to bank with Citizens."

"Would you like eight tickets to watch the game from our air-conditioned box?" she asked.

"Indeed I would," I said, as my pals looked on in awe.

The point of this story is, I am a guy that things happen to – that includes what I am sure is the ultimate, final flashing instant that each of us will experience. Ironically, it may be the only universally shared human moment. I am speaking of what happens to us when time stops.

Some years ago, a day after being subjected to what used to be called open heart surgery, my heart stopped beating. I will tell you how you recognize your last moment. A blinding white flash like the whitest of white phosphorous shells explodes in your head. That's it. It's over.

For me, even this event did not come without later coincidence.

Ten years after my heart-stopping experience, I was operated on for cancer of the head and neck. The operation was performed brilliantly by a doctor who is associated with the Dana Farber Cancer Institute in Boston. Dana Farber is now affiliated with three other nearby Boston hospitals. The operation was undertaken at the Deaconess Hospital. It was long and quite complex. When I regained consciousness I was wheeled into a room with nurses waiting. I knew I must looked frightening, but one of the nurses

2

– a blonde – kept staring at me. Even in my fuzzy state, I remember my concern increasing.

Suddenly she burst out, "I know you, you tried to die on me years ago – I know you. I remember working so hard on you – I kept saying, 'You're not going to die on me.' It took us a long time to get you back – but we did. You didn't die on me. And there is something else," she said. She pushed the call button and told somebody to get So-and-So and So-and-So to come to the room. The room became crowded as my wife and children and more nurses came in.

"Do you remember this man?" the blonde asked her comrades.

One of the girls spoke, "He's the fellow that sent the case of champagne."

"That's right," the blonde said triumphantly. She spoke now to my family. "I've been here over fifteenyears. We've all worked together on intensive care for years. This is the only person in all those years that ever sent a gift."

As I drifted off, holding Polly's hand, I think I heard the blonde say, "Your husband will get the most attention any patient ever got here."

I'm sure I did.

This book is about things that happened to me and my friends. I believe that all of them are true.

"War is sweet to them who know it not."

*English Proverb*

# Pearl Harbor Day

Today is Pearl Harbor Day. The papers and TV have pictures of old geezers saluting or placing wreaths on gravesites so America will remember what happened out in the Hawaiian Islands well over a half a century ago. I'm sure those folks and most of us who were alive on that day remember it well. I sure do.

It was bitter cold that Sunday. Bright, sunny, cold. Our gang was being allowed to go to the movies. The Park Theatre was one of two movie theatres in our town. The other was called the Strand. Neither was at all elegant, but we didn't know that.

The fact is, I had probably been inside those alluring places only once or twice. I was eleven years old and going to the movies was a big deal. The church had lists of movies you could see and couldn't see. Once a month at Mass they passed the list out. In our house and neighborhood, they were read and obeyed. We lived in an Irish immigrant neighborhood. I would guess now, looking back, that in the fifteen or twenty closely built houses at our end of the street, my mother and father were the only American-born couple.

We were all in St. Mary's Parish, which was the domain of rugged, irascible Father Curran, who had been known to knock a fresh-mouth kid on his ass and to bellow, "You did what?" inside the confessional so loud you could hear it all over the church. It was because of Father Curran that in later years some of us went to the Polish church to confession, to Father Nadolski, who spoke little English and understood less. Nobody in our neighborhood would defy a list promulgated by Father Curran – forget the Pope.

Of course the question of money came up when the movies were mentioned. All of our gang peddled papers; I raised chickens and sold eggs along with the papers. The money I earned went to the family. My mother put every dime I earned into a savings account in my name at the Cooperative Bank. She did the same with the allotment check I sent home when I was in the Marines.

So despite the fact that each of us kids had earned the eleven cents that we spent for a ticket, and the nickel or dime that went for popcorn or candy, that expenditure was serious in 1941. So as I said, a trip to the movies was a big deal.

Chilled from the cold, we went in and took off our hats and mittens. I'm sure I bought some popcorn, Eggsy Graney would go for Tootsie Rolls, Yosh Daly jelly beans, Joe Daly a Hershey Bar, my brother, Good 'n Plenties. The Flynn brothers – Tommy and Bill – I think were Milk Dud devotees.

In those days, eleven cents bought a lot of entertainment. There would sometimes be a serial film for openers. The last scene was always one where the heroine or hero, or both, were in an awful fix – one moment from doom – come back next week and see what happens. There would be the "March of Times" with the guy with the great deep voice. Then we sat through two – count 'em – two films. All of it better than any television I've ever seen.

It was late afternoon when we left the theatre. It had snowed – four or five inches of dry, fluffy snow. We went down Green Avenue, walking in the middle of the street, kicking the snow, it would fly up in the air in puffs and drift down. Green Avenue was a street of wooden row houses along one side; low railings on the short porches separated the houses. As we meandered our way down the street, folks were coming out on the porches talking with their neighbors. Some seemed uneasy as they looked up and down the street. I remember some of the women rubbing their hands nervously on their aprons.

When we got to the corner of Jefferson Street, Herbie Schindler came out of his house. We knew him from peddling papers. He was older than us, maybe fourteen. He was a big, awkward, reddish-haired kid. A hard worker. He had an extensive paper route which he handled himself. His family came from Germany.

Some folks said his father fought in the World War. I used to study him and wonder about that and what that was like when I'd see him going along the street carrying his lunch pail – a big-shouldered man with long strides. He worked at the bike factory, I think. It wasn't a dirty job like the foundry where the Irish worked. I wondered if he ever met Mr. Wesson who lived up at the head of our street, who used to sit on the front steps of his house on sunny days. That was the best he could do; he'd been gassed by the Germans in the Great War. Whatever that was about, I didn't understand, and although this wasn't our neighborhood, I knew that people liked and respected the Schindlers.

Herbie Schindler was a quiet kid. We'd stand in line to get our newspapers and there would be all kinds of fooling around – *grab-ass*, it's called in the Marine Corps. None of that for Herbie. He was always all business. He'd take his papers with just a nod. The pile was so big he needed two of the canvass carrier bags we had that said *Springfield Daily News* on the side. He would crisscross those heavy bags across the rear wheel of his bike and off he'd go without a word; just a grunt to get the bike started.

Today Herbie was a chatterbox. He had big news. America was at war. The Japanese were bombing some place out in the Pacific Ocean that was owned by the United States. Some islands out there in a place called Pearl Harbor.

He told us that the men on the radio said people in California were running around with guns looking for Japanese spies. Herbie was excited when he told us that men in the neighborhood were going to take the bus to Springfield the next day to join up. "Gosh," he said, "I hope the war lasts long enough so I can get in it."

We stopped dawdling through the snow and raced home. War – wow! Who wouldn't want to get in it?

When I got home, I found our kitchen so jammed with folks that there was a spillover in the dining room. It seemed like everybody in the neighborhood was there. My father was the guy a lot of neighborhood men came to for advice. Now excited men and women with drawn faces stood chatting. The house was full of the sound of Irish brogues. People were shushed when something new came on the radio which was tuned up loudly on its perch on the shelf over the kitchen table.

My mother grabbed my brother and me when we came in breathless with excitement and cold. She hugged us both until I was embarrassed with all the men watching.

My father had a map spread out on the kitchen table. He was pointing out where the Hawaiian Islands were and explaining to the folks the answer to the repeated question, "What in the name of God does this place we never heard of have to do with us?"

My father was known to one and all as "Chick." My mother kept her hands on my brother and me. "Chick," she asked across the crowd, "does this really mean war?"

He answered by looking up from the map and giving her a withering look. "Of course," he said.

The next day my father and all but the oldest men on the street went downtown to the Post Office to see about joining up. I skipped school for the only time in my life and, since Mr. and Mrs. Graney both worked, we all listened to the radio at Eggsy's house. We heard President Roosevelt talk to the Congress and ask for a declaration of war. This was our war too.

At supper that night, my dad glumly announced that he had been told he was too old and had too many dependents to be taken in the service. My mother ducked into the pantry after he told us, and I saw her bless herself.

My paper route became a daily trip of drama. Mothers waiting for letters; women sharing with the paperboy their sadness and fear. I remember some telegrams coming; a couple of guys prisoners of war; a number of wounded. I had about eighty-two customers. It seemed that almost every house had the blue flag with the white square and the red star in their window that signified a family member in the service. Many had more than one star. By the time the war ended, three of the houses had flags with gold stars.

When I picked up my papers at Christmas time in 1944, Herbie

Schindler's picture was on the front page of the paper. He was wearing his Army cap at an awkward angle. He had been killed in action in a big battle near the German border. They called it the Battle of the Bulge.

The war had lasted too long for Herbie Schindler.

# Missing a Rendezvous
# with History

Note: This is an expansion of an obituary that I wrote for the *Nantucket Inquirer Mirror*

He's gone. For many of us, the Nantucket summer sun won't be quite as warm, the beach won't sparkle as it did, and for me there will never be a conversation over a can of beer that will be alternately as challenging, intense, or hilarious.

If you didn't know Paul, you might remember seeing him in his later years sitting on a bench at the Athenaeum in his well worn Irish knit sweater smoking an equally worn cigar, reading the newspapers. With what he occasionally somberly referred to as his "advancing patrician forehead" and the tufts of white hair fringing his ruddy face, he was to movie fans of the 30's and 40's a look-alike to the kindly character actor Guy Kibbe.

I suppose it is fitting that Paul could be mistaken for a character actor. He was a character in the most positive use of that term. Paul earned two nicknames in his too-short life: He was known as "Pobo" to the many young people who were fascinated by him. I never knew an adult who could even approach Pobo's skills in dealing with young people. He was incontestably the best. He never spoke down to kids. He was never censorious. He treated children with dignity and equality. Young people loved his company.

To others, Paul was known as "the Colonel" in tribute to his World War II service in the Marine Corps.

Whether it was as Pobo or the Colonel, two words would be appropriate in describing Paul Burns. He was a talker and a lover. As for being a lover, many of us can speak to that. The objects of his love were many. If you had been on the patio of 129 Main

11

Street late one night last August, as the moon started to nose down over Mataket, you would have heard the Colonel tell his wife that the fifty years of marriage they were celebrating that night was a tribute to the love and support she had brought to him. No love song I've ever heard could exceed his words that night.

Pobo has five daughters. He loved them and their children with a steady, unrelenting pride. And then there is his grown grandson, Alex, who thrilled his grandfather playing football for the Nantucket Whalers and then capped that by serving with honor as a non-commissioned officer in his Grandfather's beloved Marine Corps in the Gulf War.

The list of his loves goes on: the law and its nuances which he practiced and perfected; his friends, I dare not try and list them; Boston College; Nantucket, every bit of it; Nantucket Whaler's football.

The sonorousness of the Latin Mass: when Father Lopes came to the hospital to bestow the last rites, the Colonel prayed in perfect Latin.

The Colonel could talk. No one who spent time in his company would dispute that. He could talk brilliantly on a myriad of subjects; in fact, he coined the phrase that I think sums up an aspect of an assessment of human nature better than any I have ever heard — when someone failed in a task, or performance, or did not meet expectations, the Colonel would shake his head and say, "You can't put a shine on a sneaker."

His memory was prodigious. He feasted on books, history, politics, biography, economics. There were no boundaries and he forgot nothing he read or studied. In fact, the Colonel was historically certified as a talker by a fellow who was a pretty good talker himself.

It happened like this: Soon after the peace was signed ending World War II, the Colonel was ordered to report to the White House. The occasion was the posthumous presentation of the Congressional Medal of Honor to a young man who had served in

Paul's outfit. The Colonel recounted sadly that he had hardly known the young man. He had been a replacement with the outfit only a few days before his heroic death.

The scene in the White House was uncomfortable – mother, father, and parish priest standing uneasily with young Marine Captain Burns. The President was not yet in the office. Paul chatted with the parents and the priest trying to make the moment easier. President Truman arrived and Pobo sensed that the President was a bit uncomfortable, so he tried to make Mr. Truman more at ease with additional chatter.

Years went by and in 1948 Harry Truman was running for election. He arrived in Boston and a heated Democratic Committee argued on matters of protocol. It was decided that Paul Burns – war hero – would have the honor of accompanying the President from his hotel room downstairs to the site of the dinner.

This was the scene in the elevator: President Harry S. Truman, one modest secret Service man in the corner, our beloved Colonel standing straight and looking down at the President. "Mr. President, I had the honor to be in your company at the White House when you awarded the Medal of Honor to...." The Colonel talked on and on while the President studied him. Finally Truman said, "Ah, I remember you. You're the talkative one."

There was another occasion when the Colonel's talking cost him a role in one of the 20th Century's most defining moments.

Pobo's pal and brother-in-law was a major in the Army Air Corps in World War II. He was considered one of our finest pilots. Today, rotund, debonair "Charlie" Sweeney is a Major General (Ret) U. S. Air Force.

Back in August of 1945, Pobo was on Saipan in the South Pacific. Through some magic, he learned that Charlie Sweeney had flown a B-29 bomber onto the nearby island of Tinian. Captain Burns arranged to hitchhike a boat ride over to Tinian to have a family reunion with Major Sweeney.

A man wearing an Army uniform without insignia offered Pobo a ride in his jeep when he reached the beach. The man told Pobo he was a scientist and gave our hero an odd look when Pobo told him he was looking for a pilot named Sweeney. He said he knew just where Sweeney was and would take him there. They arrived at a big open-sided tent where a lively celebration was in progress. Shouts of amazed delight when the two pals saw one another added to the feeling of comradeship in the group.

Young Captain Burns looked around and quickly realized he had never seen so many brass hats in one place. Generals, admirals, colonels were thick on the ground. More importantly, he noted some enlisted men working as bartenders on some planks set on ammo boxes and cases of beer and what looked like real ice in wash tubs.

"What the hell is going on here, Charlie?"

"Let's grab some beers and take a walk," Sweeney said. "I've got something to show you and tell you."

With beer in hand, they walked a short distance to a long metal hangar. There were military police every few yards around the building. Major Sweeney was obviously known to them as he was saluted by name by the sergeant in charge. Charlie opened a door and led his brother-in-law inside the building. They walked a few steps and stopped. There was no need for Charlie to point, there was only one object in the building.

Years later Paul Burns said to me, "Jack, I looked at that thing – I'd smelled a lot of powder by that time – thought I was reasonably tough, but just looking at the God-damned thing scared me. It was evil – you knew it was evil. Huge, black with a big fat rounded-off nose, fins – you could tell it was some kind of bomb – sitting on this dolly with great big rubber tires – all kinds of wires. I asked Charlie what the hell it was. He said it was called an atomic bomb. Said that some of those guys back at the beer party helped make it. "This thing will end the war, Paul. It's the most destructive weapon that's ever been made."

Pobo said it was one of the few times in his life he was speechless (I believe that).

Charlie Sweeney did the talking, and he's good at it too. "We dropped one of these day before yesterday on Japan – place called Hiroshima. Recon shows we leveled the place. I flew the lead.

Colonel Tebbets carried the bomb. You'll meet him. Great guy. Tomorrow they're gonna put that thing in my plane and I'm gonna' drop it. This ought to end the war, Paul. I don't think you guys will be going ashore on any more islands." Sweeney turned and spoke into the awed silence, "You wanna' come on the flight with me tomorrow?"

"I sure as hell do. There ought to be a Marine aboard that plane."

"Okay, I'll bring you with us."

Charlie Sweeney did not tell his brother-in-law that the bomb they had just looked at would be armed when it was put aboard his plane. This was unlike the Hiroshima bomb which was armed when it neared the target. Charlie's bomb would be alive before take-off. This bomb would have to be dropped somewhere. He also did not say – because he did not know – that America had two atomic bombs. It had dropped one and it worked. Paul Burns had just seen the other one.

Fortunately, the ban-the-bomb folks after the war never found out about the big beer blast that followed the Hiroshima explosion.

The party went on for a long time. Some of the men there had been waiting a long time for reasons to celebrate. One of them was a small, sandy-haired handsome man wearing the uniform of a wing commander of the Royal Airforce. His tunic carried many ribbons, but alone on the top was a crimson ribbon with a bronze cross – the Victoria Cross, England's highest award for bravery. This man was already a legendary hero of England's war against Germany. His name was Leonard Cheshire and he was the personal representative of Prime Minister Winston Churchill at these atomic doings.

Paul Burns' father was as small as his son was large. He had been born in Ireland, grew up in Liverpool in England, and settled and raised his family in America. Paul heard many stories from his father about growing up Irish in England. I don't think Pobo disliked "Limeys" or anybody, but he liked to kid the British and here was an honest-to-God English hero he could bedevil.

15

First, however, there was beer to be drunk and in my experience, no one anywhere, South Pacific, North Pacific, South or North America, England, Ireland, anywhere, no one could match Pobo at drinking beer.

I will digress for a moment to give testimony regarding my friend's international reputation as a beer drinker. A good friend of Paul's was a Navy officer and at the war's end found himself in North China where Marines were standing between the Nationalists and the Communists. He realized that Paul's outfit was in the area, so he went looking for him. He was told his regiment had taken over the local warlord's house. He inquired there of the only person he found, the little Chinese boy standing on the veranda. He worked hard to describe the Marine officer. Even then Pobo was beginning his majestic belly. Finally the little boy understood. "Ah," he beamed, "Captain Thousand Beer," he managed to say in his fractured English.

So Captain Thousand Beer went into action at the atomic bomb celebration and as the beer flowed, so did some barbed conversation between the captain and wing commander – one day to become Baron – Cheshire. Our hero had a song he loved to sing. Where he picked it up, I don't know, but he felt it was perfect for this occasion. He always sang the tune with a marvelous Cockney accent. He dropped his bomb now and watched Prime Minister Churchill's representative wince:

> I don't want to be a soldier,
> I don't want to go to war;
> I'd just rather hang around
> Picadilly Underground
> Living off the earnings of some
> 'ighborn laidy
> I don't want a bayonet up me rectum
> I don't want me buttocks shot away

I'd rather stay in England,
In merry, merry England
And roger all me bloody life away . . .
G'or blimey!

Monday I touched her on the ankle,
Tuesday I touched her on the knees
Wednesday with success, I lifted up her dress,

I have censored the next half-dozen lines because I hope my grandchildren will read these stories. So we will end with the chorus that Pobo sang on and on through the smiling years.

I don't want to be a soldier
I don't want to go to war,
Call out your royal territorials,
They'll face danger with a smile
Call out the members of the old brigade,
They'll set England free
Call out your mother, your sister
and your brother
But for Christ's sakes, don't call me!

At some point, Wing Commander Cheshire (who converted to Catholicism after the war and opened a series of orphanages known as "Cheshire Homes" throughout the British Isles) made it very clear he did not like the song. That, in fact, he was offended and did not want to hear any more. Naturally, our hero sang even louder and began a reprise. The smaller Englishman quickly made it clear that he was not intimidated about taking on the big

American. The two men had to be separated. Slightly cooler heads put a stop to this un-funny business.

The weather on Tinian the next day, August 9, 1945, was a re-run of every travel agent's depiction of the South Pacific. Hot, baking sun with a slight breeze. A perfect day to fly off and drop an atomic bomb – somewhere.

Charlie Sweeney's plane was nicknamed *Bock's Car* and it was ready to fly, the bomb installed and armed. Paul Burns, Captain USMCR, carefully climbed aboard. A last detailed inspection of the plane was made by a group of senior officers, including Wing Commander Leonard Cheshire. He looked at Captain Burns sitting sweating on the floor. "What is that man doing here?" he demanded.

"Well, Wing Commander, he's my brother-in-law. I invited him to come on this mission."

"Is he on the list of authorized observers?"

"No, sir."

"Then he must get off this plane. He cannot go on this mission."

A U.S. Air Force Brigadier General with Cheshire snapped, "Absolutely. Off. Sorry, Major Sweeney."

Captain Paul Burns carefully climbed off *Bock's Car* and out of history.

If you know a young person who can work a computer and you ask to look up Nagasaki, you will find the following:

NAGASAKI, city, Japan, western Kyushu Island, capital of Nagasaki prefecture, at the head of Nagasaki Bay. Nagasaki Bay, about five Km (about 3 miles) long and sheltered on all sides, is one of the best natural harbors of Japan. The city has important coal mining and fishing industries, ship yards and steel works, and plants manufacturing electrical equipment. It is the site of Nagasaki University (1949). On August 9, 1945, during World War II, three days after Hiroshima was destroyed, a U. S. Army Air Force plane released an atomic bomb on Nagasaki. About one third of the city was destroyed, and according to U. S. estimates, 40,000 people were killed or missing. A memorial now marks the location where the bomb exploded.

That is part of America's history. Paul Burn's is part of mine.

I will never forget the years of pleasure this man gave to me and my family and to everyone he met on his unforgettable march through life.

As I start to put down my pen, I remember the last time I ever heard my father laugh was on a long gone afternoon when he and the Colonel were enjoying a drink on the patio at 129 Main Street. I stood motionless, looking out at them from the kitchen and thought, "Gosh, my Dad loves being with Pobo."

In fact, we all did – except Wing Commander Leonard Cheshire, V.C.

# Out of the Blue

A fellow I know was a Marine fighter pilot in the Second World War. Late in the Pacific war the last big battle – the biggest battle in the Pacific – was being fought on Okinawa. My friend was flying a plane known as a Corsair off a small aircraft carrier. They were providing close air support to the Marines on the beach.

One afternoon, after their work of bombing and strafing was done, with the sun still high and fierce in the sky, he prepared to turn and follow his two wingmates back to their carrier. They had climbed high to avoid Jap aircraft on their way home.

Just as he started his turn, a flash of metal below caught his eye. He tilted his aircraft for a look. It was a Japanese airplane – the now legendary Zero. My friend put his plane's nose down and headed for the Zero, which he quickly realized was aiming at an American destroyer. This was a kamikaze pilot about to turn himself into a human bomb by flying his plane into the destroyer. Our man in the Corsair blew the Zero out of the air moments before it struck the destroyer.

Years went by – many years – and one night the phone rang at the old pilot's house. It was a man calling. He said he would like to ask the man some questions. "Are you the man who was a Marine fighter pilot? Were you in action in the Pacific during the Okinawa campaign? Did you shoot down a Zero on May 6, 1945? Was the Zero attacking a destroyer?"

Finally our friend cried halt. He had a couple of questions. "Who was this man? What was this all about?"

The caller identified himself as a retired Navy captain. He had been commanding officer of a destroyer off Okinawa in the spring of 1945. His ship had been shelling Japanese positions on the island when it had been attacked by a Zero that was apparently intent on a kamakaze mission. The ship had been saved when a

Marine fighter plane appeared out of the blue and blew up the Zero before it hit the ship.

He explained that his shipmates were having a reunion. He had been asked to do the research necessary to find out who flew the Corsair that shot the Zero that saved the ship.

"You, sir," the captain said, "are that man and we would like to honor you at our reunion. Please come as our guest with your wife and family. We will pay all your expenses. We very much want you to be with us."

Our hero has a very large family, so he decided that the fair thing to do for the reunionists was to include only his wife in their celebration. The curious couple flew to San Diego. They were met at the airport by the captain and his wife and generally treated like royalty.

The reunion was held in a beautiful terrace room overlooking the harbor. During the cocktail hour, everyone made a point of introducing themselves to the old flier and his wife and reliving that dramatic moment when he swooped down out of the blue and destroyed the Zero that was headed right at them.

When the sumptuous dinner was finished it was time for toasts. The former captain of the ship spoke of how proud he had been to command such fine men and what a wonderful experience it had been to serve with them. He said his experience aboard the ship had been the highlight of his naval career, and then he spoke of how near a firey death many of the company were on that long gone May day. He thanked my friend.

Speaker after speaker spoke of their memories of the war in the Pacific, of their fine captain and shipmates, and of the close call they had had that day. The plane exploding in air so near and yet far enough away to avoid serious injuries.

Finally a thin bespectacled man rose. "No one knows better than I what a close call we had that day," he said. "No one knows better than I the fear that was in so many of my shipmates." He paused and looked around at the silent but puzzled comrades. "Perhaps you have forgotten, gentlemen. I was the laundry officer."

# A New Deal

One of my pals I see every year at the Paw Sox baseball game is Jim Mourkas – a splendid fellow in every respect. He should have been a writer because he gets his wit and irony on paper in a masterful way. He is such good company and it comes across in his notes to me.

Jim Mourkas is the son of immigrant Greeks. He did not speak English until he was sent off to the first grade.

Jim had been in the Army before he came to Yale. And there's a story he tells that I hope you'll like.

He was with the original army of occupation in Japan, and when his two-year stint was up, he got on a troop ship to come home. Like many Greeks I know, Mourky loves to gamble, and there is no place more suited for extended gambling than a troop ship. It's probably where the idea came for floating casinos.

Corporal Mourkas was flush with money when he left Japan. However, things did not go well for him with either cards or dice. For some reason, the ship stopped for liberty in Shanghai. Mourky got off the ship with a group of his buddies with a five dollar bill as his only key to happiness in this wild Chinese port. There were six or eight comerades with Jim as he walked along the quay. In the distance he spotted a neon sign that proclaimed **New Deal Cafe**. "Boys," he said, "I'm going to give you a chance to make some money from me. I'm going to bet you each ten dollars that that cafe down the way – where the sign is – is owned by a Greek." The idea that there would be a Greek restaurant on the docks of Shanghai caused considerable mirth to his fellow soldiers. Each one of them whipped out ten dollars and bet on the ownership of the cafe.

Mourky was now in a position to have to cover everyone else's ten dollars with his own five. He was somewhat anxious as they approached the door of the cafe.

Inside the door, standing by the cash register was a fellow who certainly wasn't Chinese and when Jim Mourkas spoke to him in Greek, the man answered him and embraced him.

When I asked Jim how he'd had the guts to make his bet, he said, "Very simple. I grew up in the Depression – there was one hero for our families. The Greeks loved Roosevelt. There were New Deal restaurants, cafes and bars in New Hampshire, Northern Massachusetts and Connecticut run by Greeks. My uncle ran a New Deal restaurant. Anywhere in the world – that sign — it had to be a Greek. That was the safest bet I ever made."

# The Bridge

Today as I write, my dear friend Sam Roughton is gravely ill in a hospital in Bath, England. I've learned to understand the ramifications of the word "gravely" – simply, and sadly, the person is near the grave.

Sam Roughton and I, in some respects, could not be more dissimilar. Despite a strong strain of Yankee in me, I have played the Irish harp for much of my life. Sam Roughton is a quintessential Englishman. We have had a close odd-couple relationship for a quarter of a century. It has been aided and abetted by his sparkling wife, Ann, who is also my friend and very close to my wife, Polly.

Many of our pals have wondered how Sam and I met. It was a curious connection. Years ago I was down in Saudi Arabia. I met a Pakistani engineer – funny how I remember his name, Iqbal, last name Rheta. He was doing free-lance work for an English engineering firm called Roughton and Partners and was full of praise for his brilliant boss, Sam Roughton.

I needed some engineering work done and England was a lot closer than America. On my next stop in England, I called Roughton and Partners and arranged to meet Sam for lunch in the very British town of Bristol. He proved to be an almost movie version of an upper-class Englishman. I had learned that voice denotes status in Great Britain. Sam had the voice and the bearing of his former life as a professional soldier. I liked him at once and as the years have marched by, our liking has grown to deep affection for Sam and Ann.

Among Sam's memorable qualities are three that captured me. He was a self-read historical scholar. A storyteller of unique quality. He polished these gifts with love of good drink – in fact, he created his own sizeable vineyard, one of the few in England, on the banks of the Cam River. Sam comes from a long line of Cambridge University graduates. His father was governor of a state in India for the Imperial Raj. Sam attended the Rugby School before Cambridge. He was very proud of being a Rugby man.

Sam's stories were pithy and witty and, I thought, very British. Two that I cherish concern his early days at the Rugby School. In the savage tradition of the British Raj, Sam was sent from India (home) to England when he was seven years old. Put on a steamer by himself, I hope with a hug and a kiss, and shipped back to the mother country to get a proper education from proper Englishmen.

One day Sam and I were discussing religion, and Sam surprised me by telling me that he had been born and baptized a Catholic. He explained that his Catholic upbringing came to a sudden end on his first Sunday at the Rugby School. A savage-voiced retired sergeant major was in charge of setting up all the various lines of boys for all activities, this included mandatory church service.

On the given day, the sergeant major barked out orders: "All Church of England boys, line up here. Jews and Catholics over there."

Sam said his young mind was made up in an instant. He entered the long line of Church of England believers and joined with them in staring over at the three or four Jews and Catholics who stood hang-dog, staring at their feet.

The other tale of life at legendary Rugby which gives a strong gust of the bitter wind that blew in the confines of that "public school" concerns a young Indian prince who arrived in midterm. Before his arrival, the headmaster assembled the school and informed them that the newcomer had been involved in a terrible tragedy. He had accidentally shot and killed his father in a hunting accident. The master made it emphatically clear that this was never to be mentioned. The boy was to be treated in a kindly and courteous manner by everyone. The tragedy was never to be mentioned – never, ever.

Sam said that before the prince's first day was over, he was known as "Baghdad."

25

In 1937, after graduating from Cambridge as an engineer, he went directly to the Army. His division fought in France when the Germans roared in in 1940. I learned from Sam that there were still British troops fighting in France after what is called "the miracle of Dunkirk," when 338,000 British and French troops escaped the Nazis because the English people rose up and crossed the English channel in sailboats, paddle steamers, yachts, fishing trawlers, any vessel that could make the trip and save some troops for England.

After Dunkirk, Sam's outfit was the last British regiment in France. Earlier in the fighting he had been decorated for bravery. His stories of the debacle of the French armed forces and the Republic itself collapsing under the German onslaught are fascinating. One story had an amazing epilogue.

Sam's outfit was retreating out onto the Cherbourg peninsula, the same place the allies would land four years later, but now it was June of 1940. A Panzer group was about to crush what was left of Sam's Scotch regiment. Lieutenant Roughton took two enlisted men with him and mined a bridge that the Germans would have to cross to close the jaws on his outfit. He waited until the bridge was fully invested by the Germans – jammed with troops and vehicles. Then he blew up the bridge.

Sam and Ann have had great pleasure visiting France. They have gone there frequently. They love the wine, the food, and the French countryside. One warm sunny day, as they motored through the Norman countryside, Sam said, "Let's go visit my bridge." So they did.

They parked on the bridge and walked back and forth in the country quiet. Sam finally decided to climb down into the ravine, and doing his engineering bit, he would look at the underpinning of the new version of "his bridge." Ann waited, looking down at the stream far below.

A large black Mercedes drove onto the bridge and parked behind the Roughton's car. A man and woman got out. They nodded to Ann and then walked slowly along the bridge. After a few minutes, the man, despite his fine looking suit and tie and well polished shoes, also clambered down into the gorge.

Ann and the woman looked at one another for a moment and the lady walked over to her. She spoke French with a heavy accent. "You are French?"

Ann answered in English, "No."

The woman spoke now in English and her comment that "We are German" was unnecessary.

For some reason that always puzzles Ann Roughton, the round-faced, dumpling woman became instantly chatty, talking to her as if they were two old *haus frau* pals. Her English was thick but fluent. "We are here because my husband insisted – because of the war – he was here – on this bridge, or a bridge that was here. He says a miracle kept him alive here. The bridge was blown up. Many were killed. He fell unhurt down there, held on to something, climbed back up alive. Later my husband – he was a colonel – served in the east, in Russia – many terrible things, but he says this was his closest call. Everyone around him dead. He came back to see this place. My husband is an engineer. He needed to see this bridge again."

Ann, who is charmingly verbal, stared in wonder at the woman. She merely uttered an occasional "oh." While Ann's mind spun with this extraordinary moment, the two women stared in silence out into the countryside or into the gorge.

Sam Roughton and the German colonel climbed up onto the approach to the bridge together. They chatted quietly as they walked to their watching wives.

The colonel spoke in German to his wife. The woman's hand went to her mouth and she stared at Sam. Then the colonel introduced his wife to the Roughtons and himself to Ann. Sam announced that he and the colonel had decided the four of them would share a bottle of wine in a nearby inn. Ann said that as she and Sam drove to the inn, she felt numb. "You told him you blew up the bridge."

Sam nodded, "I did."

Ann said, "I can't believe this is happening."

The English couple and the German couple shared a bottle of wine. The men spoke of their engineering businesses; the women talked briefly of families and then stared at the men. The war was never mentioned.

When they parted, the former British and German officers exchanged business cards. Very proper, very polite.

I asked Sam if he would ever get in touch with the German. "No," he said, "and he won't contact me either."

# What Have You Been Doing Since the War?

When Sam Roughton returned to England after the French defeat, he became a commando parachute officer. He spent some time as an instructor at the commando school in the north of Scotland. He ended the war as the commanding officer of a Gurkha parachute battalion. He said the Gurkhas were embarrassed about having to use parachutes to jump out of airplanes.

The Roughtons left the army around 1950 and moved to Kenya where Sam bought a farm next to Isaak Denison and created a flourishing engineering business in Nairobi.

After many happy years in Africa, the Mau Mau rebellion brought chaos to their lives. Ann Roughton said it was no fun to carry a weapon all the time and to sit with it aimed at the kitchen door when the servants brought food into the dining room. One of the Mau Mau patterns was to follow the servants into the room and kill the family.

So after more than twenty years, it was back to England for Sam and Ann and their children. They had been out of the mainstream of the western world for a long time. They bought an ancient barn on the banks of the Cam River and turned it into a unique home that Polly and I both came to love. The house is called Cambarn.

This story is all headed to a scene in a very elegant restaurant bar in London. Sam and I had had a long business lunch and we were now relaxing with talk and drink. We relaxed into the early evening – or very late afternoon, if you're explaining things to your wife. A very swanky crowd came into the bar – some stunning women in evening dresses and handsome men in tuxedos. One of the men, the handsomest, was David Niven. The group seemed to dazzle in the deliberate soft burnished light of the cafe.

Sam and I were sitting in a corner watching these elegant people. Neither of us spoke. I was enjoying the scene. David Niven looked over at us briefly, and then looked again. He came slowly across the room, head cocked a bit, eyes narrowed. Suddenly he smiled. "Could that be Major Roughton?" he said.

"It is," Sam said, looking up. David Niven's friends, of course, had followed him across the room and now surrounded our table. David Niven turned to his friends and said, "This man was my instructor at the commando school. He was quite a warrior and a fine officer. Do you remember me?" he said to Sam. "I'm David Niven."

Sam got to his feet with his hand outstretched, "Of course I do. Niven, how are you?"

"Fine," replied the actor. "I'm very pleased to see you."

"Well," said Sam, "what have you been doing since the war, Niven?"

David Niven had the graciousness to burst into laughter and insisted on us joining his group for drinks.

# Objects In Mirror Are Closer Than They Appear

*—General Motors*

# Premonitions

My father died very suddenly. He went into the bedroom to lay down. My mother was in the kitchen. She said she heard strange noises. She thought the television in the bedroom was not working right. What she was hearing was the sound of my father struggling with an aneurysm exploding. My father was seventy-nine. He had become shaky on his feet and his voice had become hoarse, but no one knew that he was walking around with a time bomb in his chest. His death was totally unexpected.

I was with a group of people in Bermuda when I got the phone call. I got an immediate special ticket flight to Boston. I was living in Nantucket at the time so I had a friend there send a suitcase with appropriate clothes to the Boston Airport. I arranged for my children to get to the town of Westfield out in Western Massachusetts where my folks lived. I rented a car and drove there at once to console my mother, my brother and his family who lived nearby, and my grieving children.

Later I went into the bedroom where less than twenty-four hours earlier my father had died. I laid out the clothes I had brought to wear at the wake and the funeral. I realized I did not have a black tie.

I went to the phone and called my brother. I asked him if he might have an extra black tie. He said he had none and was about to call me to check Dad's ties. He held the phone while I looked.

On the tie rack were two brand new black knit neckties with the price tags still attached. They were from my father's favorite clothing store in Springfield, the big city ten miles away. In a daze I went to the phone and told my brother. "My God," was all he was able to say.

I went into the kitchen holding the ties in my hand. I showed them to my mother. She took the ties into her hands very gently and sank into a kitchen chair. She stroked the ties as she spoke.

"Day before yesterday, I knew he didn't feel well and he looked awful. He said he had to go to Springfield, I asked him not to go – wait for a day or two. He said it couldn't wait. It was important and he had to do it right away. Nothing I said could stop him. It was something he had to do himself."


My mother stayed on in the house. My brother and his wife and seven children were only a few blocks away. They were wonderful to her but in every way she tried to stay – as she would put it – "as independent as a hog on ice."

Mary Louise Howard knew how to be independent. She was orphaned as a young girl. Her older brother and only sibling was a hard drinker as a young man. He took off for the bright lights of vaudeville. My mother was taken in by the Sisters of St. Joseph. She went to work every day from the convent. It wasn't until after my mother died that I figured out one of her deepest secrets. The eighth grade was as far as she got in school. One would never have guessed that from her conversation or range of interests.

Mary Howard had a beautiful soprano voice. The nuns tried hard to find the money to send her to a coach so that she could pursue a career in classical music. That money was never found and offers to sing in clubs were vetoed by the nuns and my mother. Classical music was something she always admired. She played the piano with great flair and sensitivity. She also could play anything by ear – whistle or hum a melody and she played it like she owned it. Though she never had the opportunity for a full-fledged professional singing career she certainly made her mark in the Catholic churches in our part of Western Massachusetts.

My mother was born to the triumph of singing the splendid soaring Latin of the High Mass of the Catholic Church.

She was in charge of the music at our parish and her voice was in demand at churches all over the diocese and beyond.

I remember how you could spot strangers in the church – they would turn and stare up into the choir loft when my mother's

33

voice filled the church. Sometimes it would make me shiver –
sitting here now in the quiet I listen and yearn to hear her voice so
full of passion as she sang "Agnus Dei," the "Ave Maria" or around
our own piano, "Danny Boy" and the lovely lilting "Won't You
Come Over to My House."

My mother never stopped singing for the family but she stopped
singing for the church and that is a bitter story.

Sundays were a big day in our house. After the last Mass a
crowd would gather, especially in the kitchen. My father was a
major player in local politics. He ran the school committee for
years and for a period he was mayor of the town.

One Sunday, I was in high school at the time, my mother arrived
just as the last of the crowd was leaving. My father was standing
by the stove. As the last person went out the door my mother
began an explanation of her tardiness as she put her music books
on the counter, and tied on an apron. I can see this scene and hear
it as though it was happening right now.

"Monsignor Kirby wanted us to try some special music and he
put in additional Latin prayers to be sung for the Morrisey funeral
Mass tomorrow."

My father spoke then: "I don't see mash potatoes on this stove.
I don't smell a roast in this oven. I'm damn sure Monsignor Kirby
isn't waiting around for his Sunday meal down at that big rectory.
You go to that phone and call him and tell him you won't be
singing at that Mass tomorrow or any other time. This music and
the church is not going to run this house."

That was it. My mother made the phone call. I still can't
believe it happened, but it did.

Years later we talked about it. "Where would I have gone?"
she said. "I had you two boys, I had no family, what could I do?"
Then she added, "I thought about it for days after and I decided
your father would never tell me what to do with my time again.
He'd get his meals on time but the rest of the time was my own.
That's why I took up golf."

And take up golf she did. I suppose the phrase "with a

vengeance" is all too applicable. She played golf every chance she had. She became president of the Woman's Golf Group and served, and I'm sure dominated, in that post for years. She became an outstanding golfer. My father had given up golf years before.

She took up bowling. She was captain of her championship team that won the title year after year. Near the end of her life she was forty years older than most of the bowlers. Anyone who dealt with my mother in her 50's, 60's, 70's, 80's or 90's would never have believed the story of the end of her singing career.

After my father's death I got into the habit of calling my mother frequently, and as the years went by it became pretty much a daily event. She would bring me up to date on Westfield news – all too often the illnesses or deaths of people she knew well. Her parents came from Ireland and had settled in the town. She knew all the players and had a wide range of friends.

My brother and his wife have seven children. She left her fingerprints on every child including my brother. She would have shrewd sharp comments on the town, its people and the world beyond. Always interested in politics, she avowed that "I always vote the man." I guarantee you that man – whoever he was, whatever he had done – was a Democrat.

On the occasions when I would miss a day or two of checking in, the calls would go something like this: I dial number – phone rings

Woman's voice – sounding somewhat wary, "Hello."

Me: "Hi. How's everything?"

"What! Who is this? Who is calling?" Sharp, suspicious tone.

Me: "Ma, it's me, your long-lost son, Jack," exasperated and showing it.

"Oh, is that you? I didn't recognize your voice." Cool.

Me, still exasperated: "I can understand that, it's been about forty-eight hours since I spoke with you."

"Well, I know you're busy." Voice barely suppresses pleasure of insertion of last needle. Conversation would then commence.

35

My mother consistently lied about her age as she got older. It cost her being listed in the *Guinness World Book of Records.*

My mother was at least eighty-six when she called me late one summer afternoon. She was all business right from the opening bell.

"Jack, you know about the law."

"Just bits and pieces, Mom, I'm not a lawyer, you know."

"But you know the law, I know you do."

"What's the problem, Mom? What's happened?"

"Well, it's against the law to put someone's age in the paper, isn't it?"

"I don't think so."

"What! I'm sure it is."

"No, it's not against the law. So tell me what's happened?"

"Well, I played golf today . . ."

"Yeah?"

"And I hit a hole in one."

"Ma, that's wonderful, congratulations. Wow, that's *great*!"

"Perhaps"

"What do you mean, *Perhaps*?"

"Well, everyone made a big to-do about it. A big crowd got together in the bar at the club. Everyone toasting me with drinks. They bought champagne."

"I hope you had some."

"I had a sip."

"Good."

"Well, it's not good. They called the newspaper and a young man came and took my picture and he's going to put my age in the story. I asked him not to, but I know he is going to do it. I want you to call them and stop it or get a lawyer."

"What age are you using today, Ma?"

"That's not funny, Jack"

"How old did you tell him you were?"

"I told him I was eighty-four."

"You did, eh. Well, you're right, we'd better hire a lawyer."

36

"Oh."

"It's against the law to lie about your age to a newspaper man."

"Jack Warner, if I could get my hands on you. . ."

"Watch it, Ma, or we'll all need lawyers."

There was so much interest in a woman of my mother's age scoring a hole in one that an immediate search of the *Guiness Record Book* was undertaken. The record was held by a women of eighty-five. When my mother was told, she didn't blink or respond – well aware that if she had told the truth, she would have been the record holder.

My mother topped off the year of her hole-in-one by captaining the winning team and having the highest score in the ladies bowling league. I would guess that she was at least twenty years older than anyone else in the league.

This new triumph caused another run of the dreaded local newspaper publicity which triggered a more ominous national intrusion.

She called me one day to let me know she had received a very disturbing phone call. I could hear the concern in her voice. She asked me if I was familiar with a program called *Sunday Morning*.

I said I certainly was; it was my favorite television program.

"Well," she said, "the station in Springfield called me and said they talked with their station in New York."

"CBS in New York?" I interrupted.

"I guess," she said. "They said they'd like to come here – here to the house – and have this man interview me for their program, about the golf and the bowling."

"Charles Kuralt. He's terrific, Mom."

"I suppose," she said.

"This is wonderful, Ma! So what did you tell them?"

"I told them they ought to have something better to do with their time and I hung up."

Shameless is a word that comes too close to fitting my mother's attitude to telling the truth regarding her age. We had two ninetieth birthday parties for her. They were two years apart.

One Friday in the spring of my mother's ninety-fourth year, I drove up to Westfield to spend the night with her. We had our usual bouts of banter and laughter and sarcasm with occasional moments of bittersweet reminiscence of days past.

The next day we went to one of Westfield's modest restaurants for lunch. I think everyone in the place came over to the table to say hello to her. She received them all in the regal manner that seemed to have become part of her. She was always a presence and in her hometown she had become an historic personage.

When we got back to the house after lunch, we went for a walk. Mom had been a big, handsome, buxom woman with great posture. Now she was a little old lady, bent over her cane, but still vigorous and vital as she moved along beside me.

Suddenly she stopped. She looked up at me and took my hand. "I want you to know," she paused. "I don't want to go." She spoke in a fierce tone. "I don't want to go." She squeezed my hand and looked piercingly into my eyes. Her eyes still had that flash of green. "You understand? I don't want to go."

"I understand, Mom," was all I was able to say. When I left she stood in the kitchen door and waved goodbye. I called her that Saturday night to tell her I was back in Chatham and how much I enjoyed our visit.

My mother said she had just been about to call me. "There's something I want to tell you," she said, and continued with a rush of words. "You have been the most wonderful son a mother could ask for. You'll never know what your kindness to me has meant. Whatever happens, don't ever forget this."

At 9:30 the next morning, my brother called me. His voice was thick. I could hear crying in the background.

"Mom is gone. We're here at the house to take her to Mass with us and we found her. She's all dressed up – ready to go – she was sitting on the edge of the bed and it happened. She's lying on her back with her feet on the floor."

# Deliver Us from Evil

On a Friday morning in a recent November, my wife and I and a group of friends from Cape Cod got on the train in Providence and went to New York for the weekend. We stayed at the Yale Club and on Saturday the men went over to Giant Stadium and watched the Yale-Princeton football game. The weekend was delightful – full of good memories.

The following Monday my wife and I drove to Boston where I had a doctor's appointment. I had been being treated for a sinus infection for some months and now a lump had appeared on the right side of my neck.

A dear friend of mine, Dr. Trevor McGill, came to America from Ireland and brought with him an overflowing bounty of benevolence and brains. Trevor is the boss of otolaryngology at Children's Hospital in Boston. He had arranged my appointment with a Dr. Norris who he referred to as "one of the best head and neck men there is."

Dr. Norris came into the examining room looking somewhat distracted, a bulky man of plus or minus fifty – I guessed more minus than plus. He had a thoughtful air about him. I noticed he was wearing basketball sneakers.

When I got to know of the time he spent in the operating room I understood why he would want to have comfortable footwear. When I learned of his skill at his profession the sneakers were even more appropriate. For indeed, Dr. Charles Norris may be the Michael Jordan of head and neck surgery. He spoke in a casual, friendly manner and it was clear to me that he was another fan of Dr. Trevor McGill.

Norris examined me in a manner that told me he was going to know everything possible about the areas of my head, nose, ears, mouth and throat that he could see with various devices. When he was through with the instruments he placed his hands on my neck and manipulated areas with his fingers – particularly the lump on the right side of my neck.

When the examination was completed he put the instruments in some sort of a sterilizing compartment. He had not spoken for some time. When he turned to face me, I sat still in the examining chair, I could read nothing in his expression. He spoke with a gentle voice. I had asked him to call me Jack and he did.

"Jack, you have cancer. There is a growth on your palate and it has metastasized into the lymph nodes in your neck."

He continued to speak but I raised a shaky hand and said in a voice that seemed to come from a long way off, "Doctor, my wife is in the waiting room. I'd like to get her so she can hear this and we won't have to do this twice."

I was stunned and feeling faint. Only months before I had helped bury my younger brother who had been killed by cancer. I started to push myself from the chair.

Norris put a very firm hand on my shoulder. "You stay there. I'll get your wife."

From the first crushing, stunning moments I think that some part of my mind that was functioning knew that my life had changed forever.

Polly came into the room without speaking. She kissed me and then sat with her hands folded. Her face was devoid of color – as I'm sure mine was – and her eyes were wide and seemed not to blink.

I remember some of what Norris told us. He said that we might be dubious of his call of cancer without a biopsy but he said he was sure the biopsy, which should be taken right away, would confirm his judgement. He said he believed the cancer was well advanced and that its primary source was on my palate. He explained the role of the lymph nodes in collecting the cancer cells as they traveled in the body. He also told us that if we wanted to get a second opinion we should know that there were at least two schools of thought regarding treatment of cancer of this type. He said that if we went to Sloan Kettering in New York we would be advised to have immediate radical surgery followed by radiation. The Boston school of thought was the opposite. Radiation – in my case, massive – followed by surgery. He offered to give us names of other medical people if we wished. I told him that if my wife agreed we would stick with him. I looked at Polly and she nodded.

Thus, just like that, we put ourselves and perhaps my life into the deft hands of Charles M. Norris, Jr. M.D.,F.A.C.S.

Driving home from the doctor's office Polly broke down. This was the only time that she cried in front of me during all of the emotional storm that we would endure. I pulled over to the side of the road and with my arms around her I told her that there was a bright spot even in this darkness. I explained that when Doctor Norris prepared to go out to the waiting room to bring her back for our conference, he asked me to describe my wife. I told him that she was short, dark and beautiful.

"Doesn't that make you feel better?" I asked.

The sound of Polly's crying became part laughter. She said, "Jack, I was the only one in the waiting room."

Two days later we returned to Boston. As Norris promised, events moved very quickly despite the fact that I felt like a sleepwalking participant. I think there were two reasons for the fast reaction. The first was medical. I'm sure Norris felt an urgency to try to stop what he had referred to as "well advanced cancer." The second, I think, was the medical fraternity. The fact that I was a close pal of Dr. McGill, the highly respected head and neck surgeon of Children's Hospital caused me to receive what one young doctor referred to as "the fastest response I've ever seen around here." There is a lesson in this – if you are unlucky enough to get sick, hope that you have enough good luck left in you to have a pal who is a significant member of the medical fraternity.

So, forty-eight hours after my first meeting with Dr. Norris I was anesthetized on an operating table at the Deaconess Hospital. Biopsies were taken from my palate and the lump on my neck. Analysis of the tissue was done as I lay there. Dr. Norris advised me when I became conscious that the growth on the palate proved to be difficult to diagnose, many cuts were made for laboratory review. Consequently, he had essentially excised that growth. The call on the aberration on the palate was uncertain and would haunt me. We would never be sure of the primary source of the cancer.

There was not any question about the lump on my neck. It was cancer. It had a name. It was deep in the lymph nodes and it was sizeable.

The day after the biopsy surgery Polly and I sat in a conference room at the Dana Farber Cancer Institute. Dr. Norris and a half dozen colleagues discussed me and my cancer. I told them that my wife would take notes since we found that we often seemed to have different versions of what doctors said to us. I didn't say that I expected to be a less than alert participant in the meeting. I was experiencing strong pain in the area of the lump on my neck.

All the medical people had opinions about dealing with my cancer. I listened to them as though they were talking about someone else. Then I realized they *were* talking about someone else. I had become another person.

I was now a citizen of the inner city of the sick. These people were my masters – all of them that I had been dealing with, nurses, doctors, attendants – all of them in their goodness and kindness knew that I was a reluctant citizen of another place who must do their bidding – or else.

I was a cancer patient. That phrase probably evokes as much emotion in people today as the leper's bell did in ancient times. But there is certainly no revulsion on the part of the caregivers. They are consistently kind and thoughtful and attentive, especially the nurses who surely are God's angels of mercy.

The conversation of the doctors seemed reasonably intelligible with occasional side bars of medical esoterica. One thing was clear to Polly and me – Doctor Norris was the boss. He did the summing up. I'm surprised at how well I remember.

Because of some other physical ailments I had, there would

be no chemotherapy. This meant that I would be subjected to double dosages of radiation. I recall that Norris said, "We will take you to the very limit of your endurance. You may experience nausea and lack of appetite. You will probably be unable to swallow and to speak for a period of time. Perhaps a lengthy period of time. I insist that you have a feeding tube inserted in your stomach right away so that you can receive nutrition and not have a dangerous weight loss. You will be fitted with a tin mouth guard to protect your teeth. Radiation can be very destructive to your teeth and your salivary glands, your taste buds will be affected, all of this may be permanent." He paused for what seemed a long time and then in the stillness he asked, "Do you want to go through with this?"

I quickly answered yes. It seemed to be the most basic question I had ever been asked. Do you choose life or death?

I would come to understand why he asked that question and I have pondered at length about what kind of an answer I would give if I were asked today.

Two days later I began the day in a dentist's office at the Brigham and Women's hospital where an imprint of my teeth was taken for the mouthpiece that would protect my teeth from the radiation that I was soon to receive. The dentist informed me that the guard would have to be made of pure tin to resist the radiation.

I went from the dentist's to a large, chilly antiseptic room dominated by a huge cream colored camera-like device that loomed over a long rectangular stainless steel table. Clearly this was the radiation machine. For a reason or reasons I cannot explain, I found it to be obscene.

A group of white jacketed folks watched me through a small window. I was directed to position myself on the cold table by one of the soft spoken, efficient technicians in the room. He told me that the radiation specialists in the viewing room would be calculating the angles required for the very tricky business of directing destructive rays on and into my palate and neck and upper chest.

I soon learned there would be a guarantor that there would be no movement on my part when the dangerous rays were fired into me. One of the attendants brought a large square of what proved to be plastic mesh over to the table. He held the fabric in front of him with his rubber gloved fingers. After warning me to close my eyes and that the material was wet and hot, but not too hot, I felt the mesh draped over my head, face and neck. The plastic was as advertised and as I wondered what was happening to me I felt fingers manipulating the mesh, smoothing it down over my forehead, my eyes, fitting it closely over my nose and chin and down onto my neck. In a short time they carefully lifted the material off me. I turned my head and watched them go to a deep sink set on the wall, immerse the mesh into a liquid, then carry it from the room. I lay there in the silent chill too numb to think.

I don't know whether I lay on the table a short time or a long time but when the caregivers returned the plastic mesh had become a rigid mask which was placed over my face. It was very uncomfortable as it was somehow latched onto the table. I could not move my head or neck – not one flinch. Some minor adjustments were made but it remained unpleasant and uncomfortable. It would remain unpleasant and uncomfortable in the months ahead.

The object, of course, was to prevent the tiniest movement of my head and neck. It was so tight that I could not simultaneously fit the upper and lower tin teeth protectors in my mouth when I tried to wear them when they arrived.

The day after I knew I was to become a masked man was Thanksgiving. Our family assembled at our house on Cape Cod.

The things that would sustain me in the months ahead were all there for me on that Thanksgiving. Family, friends and prayer.

There is a shock that comes when a family member has cancer. It is an earthquake that strikes the family, every member feels the tremor. I think that mixed with pity and sorrow for the victim is a deep down genetic foreboding. There is an awful sense that no one is safe. Death is now publicly stalking the people you love and perhaps you too. To the family the word cancer means death. That word is never spoken but its presence is palpable and grinding. The strange bonus in this tragedy is that it allows some family members to show their love for the victim in a way that might never have occurred if the dread sentence had not been passed. The sense of the family circling the wagons to protect me brought an aura of well-being to me that defied the cancer.

Cancer provides an awful opportunity to test every aspect of your being. You cannot hide from yourself. You are forced to look at every facet of your character. It became for me a time to look at things done and left undone – to remember acts of foolishness or unworthiness. It could have been a time of deepest depression. I found that prayer was a barrier to the demon depression.

My friends also manned the ramparts to defend me. Their consistent kindness and thoughtful reaching out to me kept me from sliding into the black hole that was now a permanent part of my landscape.

The first act of blessed kindness came early – Goodness and the evil of cancer were beginning their deadly battle. Polly and a pal of ours were rushing around Boston looking for a furnished apartment to use as a base camp for the climb we were preparing to endure. A dear friend named Betty Nolan, once a midwife in the west of Ireland, stepped in. This saintly, stalwart woman put an immediate stop to the apartment search. Her elegant house in Brookline is ten minutes from the Dana Farber, Deaconess, Beth Israel complex of hospitals where I would be radiated and operated on. We would stay in her house. I would have her bedroom. She made her house our home for months.

A long, loving line of our friends visited frequently and at all hours – every one of them greeted warmly by our hostess and her lovely daughters. Food and drink for all were always available in Irish quantities. The Warner family will never be able to put a price on their act of love.

I came to think, as the campaign went on, that perhaps love is cancer's most powerful enemy.

45

The days passed in a numb haze. The rigid mask latched me to the table for a few minutes every morning except some Saturdays and Sundays. For a brief while I thought I was impervious to the rays of the giant machine. But soon all of Dr. Norris's predictions became part of my existence. The feeding tube in my stomach took the place of knife and fork and spoon. Salivary glands stopped working. Speech became difficult and then impossible.

My body was under assault and I could read the results in the looks on the faces of new visitors. My very being was changing. My mind and my body. I never realized while it was happening that some of the changes were permanent. I don't believe one can experience cancer and be the person you were before the diagnosis. That may also be true of our loved ones.

The phrases we hear as children – "take this and you'll feel better" and "do this and you'll be better soon" – are axioms that we lock onto and carry with us into grown-up land; but they don't hold with cancer citizens of the inner city of the sick. I'm not sure any of us believe, truly, that after our treatment we are "all better."

Yet, fellow cancer sufferers do not acknowledge this to one another. I have never met such resilient, proud, defiant battlers as my fellow victims. The mood in the radiation waiting room is consistently upbeat. There are smiles and plans for the future and encouragement of one another and light hearted chitchat that prevent silences from becoming leaden.

I learned that the victims of cancer form a noble brotherhood. There is no awareness of race, of status – money has lost its power. We are all supplicants before whatever deity we choose – be it dice or deus.

From the day of Dr. Norris's diagnosis I had been revulsed by the lump on my neck. My shaving was now done with an electric razor because the metallic properties in shaving cream become dangerous when hit with radiation. I never went near that part of my neck. But both night and day I would sneak a look at the lump. It didn't get smaller.

As I write this I have absolutely no memory of that Christmas.

However, New Year's Eve is indelibly imprinted on my memory. Doctor Norris, like so many key players in the medical profession, is often stretched thin. So it was not until early evening on that dark and cheerless New Year's Eve 1997 that the good Doctor gave me my weekly examination. As he was manipulating the lymph nodes on both sides of my neck and in particular, the tumor on the right side, we were eye to eye.

"Doctor," I managed to whisper, "I've had a lot of radiation, haven't I?"

"You sure have", he said. "I'm afraid you're getting fried."

"That thing isn't diminishing, is it?" I said.

It seemed a long time before he responded. I remember he was very noncommittal.


Charlie Coudert was a classmate and teammate of mine at Yale. Charlie is a patriot who has served his country with distinction wearing a number of different hats since the day he graduated. He is also an intellectual and a deeply devout Catholic gentleman. Charlie and his wife, Roby, were among the many who were a prayerful and peace-bringing presence to me during my illness.

Sometime in the early winter Charlie mentioned a priest named Father Francisco Paco who was reputed to have healing powers. He asked me if I would be interested in meeting Father Paco and I said that I would.

In mid-January, on a cold drizzly day, Polly and I completed my task at the radiation lab and returned to our safe house in Brookline. In the afternoon the rain had turned to sleet and Charlie Coudert drove me out to Sherbourne to a friend's house to meet Father Paco. I can't say what I expected to happen. I am surprised, even now, that I remember what the weather was like that day because by that time days, nights, sunshine, darkness, rain or snow didn't seem to be part of my life.

Father Francisco Paco is a slim, young man of Mexican

heritage. Since my voice was pretty well gone, his attempt to chat with me was brief. Charlie explained my illness to him. Father Paco asked if I would pray with him and I nodded. Without any prior plan I found myself on my knees. Charlie knelt beside me. Father Paco put his hands on my head and began to pray. His words were very gentle. Suddenly, I began to weep. I had not shed a tear at any time during my agony but now silently, totally and uncontrollably, I wept.

Father Paco finished, he and Charlie helped me to my feet, I shook his hand and went out into the weather. I had not been able to speak to him. I was choked in tears and sadness. When we got in the car I turned to Charlie to apologize for my lack of control and I saw that tears were streaming down his cheeks.

During a night after this experience – I can't remember how many days had passed, one or two or three – I awoke and found myself scratching at the tumor on my neck in a vigorous, agitated way. The lump itched and I was scratching it. This reaction frightened me. I had never touched the tumor since I had been told that it was cancerous. Finally I dozed off, puzzled and worried and exhausted.

In the morning in the bathroom while feeding myself with the stomach tube, I looked in the mirror. I capped the tube, turned sideways and looked closer. I hurried out of the room to get Polly and show her what had happened. The lump was gone. It wasn't there.

Soon after, during his next inspection, as Dr. Norris put his hands on the sides of my neck, his eyes widened and he said quietly, "Something dramatic has happened here."

As his fingers probed the lymph gland, he spoke – almost to himself – and said, "You know if I brought an experienced colleague of mine in here, I'm not sure he would be able to find any mass."

I did not tell Dr. Norris about Father Paco.

Dr. Norris was more open with me at that moment than I had been with him. The good man looked me straight on and said, "I want you to be aware of two mean possibilities that can occur during this surgery." He then explained what, I guess, might be described as the anatomy of the area he would be operating on. I think I perhaps consciously half heard him, but his final words got my full weary attention: "Depending on the structure and proximity, it is possible that you may lose your ability to speak and it is also possible that you may lose the use of your right arm."

I don't know if there was a long pause or not. I do know I whispered my understanding and assent.

On the 26th of February Dr. Norris and his colleagues preformed a Radical Neck Dissection on me at the Deaconess Hospital. They started early in the morning and finished in the evening.

My first memory is of a group of doctors looking down at me, telling me to move my tongue and speak – and then to move my right arm. I did those two things.

Doctor Norris reported that deep in my neck, much deeper than they had guessed, he found a pecan sized object filled with a liquid. He was clearly pleased with the results of the operation and was optimistic about my recovery.

The day I left the hospital I decided to share my religious experience with my medical man. When I finished telling the story of Father Paco and me, Dr. Norris was quiet. Finally he said to me, "When I began in this work if you had told me that story I would have shrugged, but now I don't know. I can tell you this," he said, "when I drove home last New Year's Eve I wasn't very optimistic about you."

# Inner City of the Sick

In December of 1997, I was very ill and I wrote a piece that my friend Mike Barnicle carried in his *Boston Globe* column on December 23rd as a Christmas message. Here it is. Mike's title was "Love Reigns in this Inner City."

We are in the hallway of a hospital, the Dana-Farber, where the excitement of the season seems distant and awkwardly inappropriate. A friend and I have come to visit a guy, Jack Warner, who has been around for a long time, right in the center of city politics for years, before retreating to Nantucket where he has lived a wonderful life.

But nobody comes to Dana-Farber for an appendectomy or flu. The building is a place where the possibility of miracles exists every day side by side with the crushing potential of mortality.

Warner is in a fine mood, despite the fact that he cannot speak and has to communicate with us using a small blackboard – as we prepare to leave, he hands us an envelope containing his own seasonal message.

"As the people of the city prepare for Christmas," Jack Warner wrote, "there is even within this place a quick acceleration to the daily movement and natural tempo of life that seems to generate a hum of excitement and anticipation one can almost feel. We think of Christmas as giving and getting, when streets and stores are crowded with customers seeking the perfect gift to help spread the magic of the season.

"There is, however, another city within the city of Boston: The city of hospitals, the true inner city of the sick, filled with those who need care and those who dispense it – the caregivers –

who walk the halls carrying their enormous cargo of gifts.

"This city is always crowded. Its residents dwell in wards and precincts as varied, blessed and cursed as all the others located in the larger urban setting around them, beyond the walls and windows of the hospital. There is a difference, however: Every day, every one of us who live here is intensely aware that we are all part of the Inner City of the Sick.

"I have recently become a resident of this city. I live in the cancer ward.

"And as I rather numbly sense preparations for the celebration of the birth of the Christ child in the big city beyond, I watch the behavior and attitude of my new neighbors with feelings of awe and revelation. I am constantly awed by the kind behavior of terribly sick, frightened people toward those around them, and I am no less touched by the caring reaction of the healthy helpers who work with us, for us, among us, like apostles.

"There is the revelation that this unfeigned courtesy and consideration between the citizens of my new city is the essence of Christmas: The caring and concern of the sick for one another are gifts from the heart that are distributed each day.

"Christ's message of hope for a brotherhood of mankind finds its ironical triumph in a waiting room for cancer treatment. There is no racial prejudice here, no envy of status or positon, no greed or thoughtlessness, no squabbling over position. Cynicism is a stranger, driven out by the deep desire to believe in the simple gifts of health and life.

"Our existence has been reduced to its most elemental form: We want to continue living. And if we receive this gift, we will, no doubt, be better able to share what has been revealed to us here in the inner city where gratitude arrives with each new dawn. In the world outside, the larger one beyond the wards of my domicile, wealth and success are measured in terms that are false and fail badly when viewed from the hallway of my new home: There is no financial market, no bank, no mutual fund that can place a proper price on items like kindness, compassion, love, memory, and care provided by people who are themselves selfless saints.

"After the tinsel is removed and the tree disappears, the simplicity and sincerity encountered within the inner city remain. And the true Christmas message never dies

"A patient solicitude is eternal here. An honest attempt to assist those most in need is quite constant. The definition of 'neighbor' and 'friend' assumes new and rich meaning.

"At night, the lights of the other city sparkle in the clear, winter distance seen from my window, the sight of Christmas-past. Along the hallways of my own inner city, there is only the vision of decent people bearing a kind smile and a warm, prayerful hope for the one thing that matters most, life. This is Christmas-present.

"Here, we have a daily celebration of love. A daily declaration of simple gifts, accepted with enormous gratitude by people humbled by the kindness shown by the most merciful souls I've ever known, the caregivers of the inner city. They represent the purity of the Christmas season. Their diligence and devotion make it Christmas each day in the shadows of the inner city of the sick."

# You Think You've Got Problems

Are all weddings referred to as "lovely"? It seems to be the adjective of choice. So I will tell you that on a particular fall weekend, we went to a lovely wedding over on Nantucket. For my money, there is no more charming place in the fall than Nantucket. In the church, the bride and groom glowed like the sunshine outside. After the ceremony, there was drink aplenty and a lavish sit-down dinner. My wife and I were seated at a place-carded table for ten.

I found myself seated between two ladies. One, a treasured old friend, the other woman I did not know well. We'd met a few times. She was neither young nor old, but attractive, and very stylish.

When I sat down, the old friend on my left and I had a lot of catching up to do. That occupied some minutes. It wasn't until food started being served that the attractive lady on my right began a rather intense conversation with me that would prove – well – you decide on the appropriate word.

I think somewhere in these pages, I have explained my problem with food. Did I tell you that I have no saliva? None. It is a harsh, frustrating experience to try to eat under these circumstances. I have found that I must have a glass of milk, preferably skim, to act as a lubricant. I've also developed a phobia about eating in front of people I don't know well because the act of trying to eat causes me to sweat very visibly on my face and head. All in all, food now means trouble for me.

I was struggling with my head down, working on the full plate of steak, salmon, potatoes and string beans that had been set in front of me. I was sure everyone at the table was staring at me.

I soon realized that one person was.

My stylish neighbor leaned over toward me and spoke quietly: "Is it that you have no taste, Jack? Is that why eating is so difficult for you?"

Despite the question I was glad to be diverted from the food. "No," I said, "I don't have much of any taste, but that's not the problem. I don't have any saliva."

"No saliva?"

"None."

"Why, I never thought of saliva as being a very important part of our lives. Isn't that strange. Imagine, saliva, of all things."

"Without it," I said, "you can't swallow food. One has to have some bit of liquid. For me, it's milk."

"Does it effect your teeth? No saliva?"

"It sure does. They need constant attention because they go to hell without saliva."

"Well," she said, "it's amazing the problems that people have that no one thinks much about."

"Yes," I agreed. My thoughts were more and more on how I could gracefully get out of there – go for a walk and come back and get Polly later.

"Well, as for myself," she continued, her head bent toward me again. "I have an awful problem. It's one that you probably wouldn't think of. Actually, I've got it under control now thanks to this holistic doctor I found, but I've had a terrible problem – I have an atrophying vagina."

I'm sure I must have blinked, or maybe rocked a bit in my chair. Did I hear her correctly? I turned and stared at her. My face must have shown – what? surprise? confusion? astonishment? Those reactions might have all crossed my features.

"Yes" she answered my look. "An atrophying vagina. I tell you, Jack, I was drying up like a prune. It's a terrible situation and I imagine it's a problem you never thought of."

"I'll tell you," I said, "it's definitely something I've never thought of. It's a problem that never crossed my mind."

At that point, I couldn't stop the impulse: I burst out laughing. My wife looked down the table with a pleased look to see me laughing. It wasn't until some time later that she knew why.

# Come Dance with Me
# In Ireland

*W. B. Yeats*

# A Day at the Races

I expect we've all had those is-this-really-happening moments. One of my most vivid came many years ago in, I suppose appropriately, Ireland.

A fellow I knew talked me into investing in a horse racing syndicate. The syndicate raised a lot of money. It was sponsored by Donaldson, Lufkin and Jenrette, which gave it some credibility; added to that was that the managing director was a horseman named Firestone. A pretty good combination, I thought, but it proved to be a scam.

But my day at the races was not a scam. Maybe it was worth the investment.

The Firestone Group had a splendid stud farm in Ireland. Horses would be bred, trained and raced in America, Ireland, England, and the Continent. I am a sucker for many things Irish and I couldn't withstand the lure of visiting the stud and watching horses that I had a piece of gambol on the lush green grass or race at the legendary race course of Ireland – the Curragh. So I paid my money and took my chance.

I couldn't get to Ireland fast enough to visit "our" stud and have a day at the races. I took my oldest son with me and a pal who had moved from Ireland to practice medicine in America.

The stud looked like Hollywood's version of Ireland: what seemed like miles of perfect stone walls, a handsome Georgian house set at the end of a long drive amidst low whitewashed stone barns. In the fields, green beyond imagination, sleek, powerful horses nibbled, posed and some ran like the wind in occasional gusts.

Mr. Firestone wasn't there, but a gourmet lunch was. We

were waited on by two fine looking, solicitous colleens. The future would tell if Mr. Firestone could pick winners in the horse game, but he sure knew fine wines and handsome young women. We cruised through a small fortune of the finest wines of France. This proved to be the only material dividend in the deal.

We had been joined at lunch with my Irish pal's great boyhood buddy, now a dentist with a practice in England where he confided he "kept three or four Pakis" on his payroll filling cavities while he made frequent visits back home to Ireland. His uncle was manager of the Curragh.

The stud had two or three horses running that day. I didn't have a winner but we did have a great time. A bright sunny day full of Irish character and characters. The weather was dry but our circumstances were not. Some mellow time after the last race the dentist's uncle, who seemed to be known and liked by everybody at the race track, suggested we go to "Donovan's Arm" out in the country for drinks and some food. He said it was a place "Yanks like you should see."

We followed the man from the Curragh for miles in our car, chatting, laughing and recounting the events of the day. As we pulled into a neat village, the dentist announced this was it. "Is it Donovan's Arms?" I asked, "or Donovan's Arm?"

"Oh, it's Donovan's Arm, alright, as you'll soon see." We pulled up near a stone building that, I think, had a thatched roof. The rest of these details I am sure of.

The pub was low ceilinged and dark. We stood just inside the door and the dentist kept us there while he gave us a talk like a tour guide. "In the early 1800's" he began, "there was a marvelous English heavyweight fighter named Smythe. No one could beat the man. He'd fight anyone and he beat everyone. He was champion of the British Empire. Bare fisted – bare knuckled – savage bloody fights. And the money that was bet – well, you wouldn't credit it! Thousands and thousands of pounds! The man and his crowd made a fortune. But we had our own champion here in Ireland – Donovan was our man and it became the great talk in Ireland and England that the Englishman and the Irishman should fight for the real championship – to see who was really the toughest man in the Empire.

"They fought outdoors in a great natural bowl in the earth right near here. Thousands came and the fight was brutal but the Englishman was no match for Donovan. Donovan near killed him with his great smashing rights. All Ireland was wild with joy.

"Donovan lived out his days in this village. He died and was buried here but after awhile the folks realized they needed something to remember him by so they dug up the hero, they cut off his mighty right arm and saved the arm that brought glory to Ireland." The dentist stopped for breath and gave us a big smile with his handsome teeth. "Now, follow me boys," he said. We marched behind him between tables and chairs to the bar at the far end of the room. There was a glass case spotlighted on the wall back of the bar – a long black sinewy object was in the case. "Here it is boys, preserved forever, the great Donovan's Arm."

We stood transfixed, staring at the object. No doubt about it, it was an arm. "That's quite an arm," my doctor friend said quietly.

I was intrigued with this extraordinary Irish trophy. I sipped my pint and studied the dark, ropey, musculature. Donovan must have been a hell of a big fellow or those once fleshy knuckles would have scraped the ground. What a protean reminder of the intense Irish-English bitterness. Here was a symbol from the grave. How proud these folks were of mighty "Donovan's Arm." The champion of the English.

Our day at the races wasn't over yet. There was someone in this village pub who had smashed more people than Donovan could ever have imagined. A round table of hail fellows had been put together by the jolly manager of the Curragh. I left off admiring Donovan's arm and took a seat. There were noisy introductions amidst a heady feeling of good fellowship. There were perhaps ten of us around the big table and my usual fuzzy reception held true when introductions were made.

I did realize that the man on my left was not Irish – definitely not Irish when I heard his guttural voice. I thought the manager had called him Otto but I wasn't sure. I turned to him and said, "I'm sorry, I didn't get your name."

"I am Skorzeni" he said simply.

He proffered his hand, which was meaty and hard with calluses. He stared directly into my eyes. He was of medium height, a blocky figure with a square jaw, close-cropped grayish hair. He was wearing a worn rumpled blue suit.

At that moment I was feeling a wave of confusion. Was this really happening? Could this man be who I thought he was? I had to ask.

"Are you General Skorzeni?"

"I am," he answered, continuing to look me straight on.

This was the man known as "Hitler's General," the commander of German parachute troops. His boldness and personal courage leading his troops in France, Crete and Russia earned him the grudging respect of his enemies. His audacious drop into the mountains of Italy to rescue Mussolini from his captors late in the war stunned the allies and got the world's attention.

Sitting beside me was a legendary warrior of the Second World War. There was another question – How would I put it. I couldn't ask him what the hell are you doing here? So I asked "What are you doing now, General?"

"I am an Irish farmer," he said firmly as he lifted his pint of Guinness.

I sat there beside General Otto Skorzeni and looked at him and then at Donovan's Arm.

It had been some day at the races.

# Special Delivery

My friend Trevor was born in a small village south of Dublin. His mother worked as a domestic in a big Georgian house owned by an Anglo-Irish family. His father, Jack, worked as a clerk in the local post office. Just for the record, Jack McGill and his wife had six children besides Trevor; six of the seven became doctors.

Ireland's unemployment was a fact of life in those years; it seemed permanent. To soften that condition, there was a postmaster and two assistants in the small office in the village. Jack McGill was one of the assistants. Knowing his son as I do, Jack must have been a charming man who brought life and wit with him wherever he went. He also was not reluctant to share a pint in good company and there was plenty of good company in the village and in the post office.

Once a year, the postal inspector came down from Dublin unannounced to make sure that all was well when he swept into the little office. He was a strict, officious soul who made sure everyone worked by the rules. He could never find any major fault with Jack McGill and his co-workers and there was a reason for that. The inspector would call ahead a week in advance and reserve a room in the old six bedroom hotel cum pub that was the center of village activity. The pub keeper, of course, quickly passed the word to Jack and his mates. The post office and its employees were always ship-shape and squared away when the inspector marched in and thought he was surprising them.

All went well for some years until, unbeknown to Jack and his cohorts, the inspector was promoted and a new man took over. This fellow did not make a reservation at the old hotel.

One morning around eleven o'clock, the new inspector sauntered into the post office. He looked around and there was no one there. He waited a while, stamped his feet a couple of times, called out, "Hello! Hello!" Nothing happened – still no one. He went to the door behind the counter and opened it – nobody in that tiny back room. Where were the stalwarts of the post office department? Ahhh – behind the counter where the workers should be in attendance, he spotted a buzzer. He put a finger on the button and pushed.

He waited and he waited.

Finally, he heard the back door open. Then the door behind the counter opened.

A young fellow carrying a tray with three dark foam-topped pints of Guinness made a delivery to the post office.

# Twasn't Locals

My wife and I love Ireland. We have a special bond there. I have cousins who live in the farmhouse where my grandmother grew up. It is on land that sits on one of God's greenest hillsides and tumbles down to the rocky shores of Dunmanus Bay. It is close to the southwestern tip of Ireland – that place in Ireland nearest to America, yet seems a world away.

On a visit some years ago, we learned that some aspects of our American world are not that far removed from Ireland.

We were traveling with our friends Jim and Rosemary Murphy. No better traveling companions ever existed. The four of us had visited the island together a couple of times before and on these occasions we made sure we visited the quintessential west of Ireland seaport town in County Kerry – called Dingle. As the Irish say, "It's a stretch of the legs to get to Dingle." The town is all by itself out on a peninsula that is hammered by the rolling, relentless Atlantic. Coming down from the North one heads southwest out of Tralee over memorably scenic mountains and glens on twisting Irish roads with sheep as the only traffic. From Killarney it's well over two hours to Dingle but if you've been there you know the getting there is time well spent.

The night before we were due in Dingle, we had an unpleasant experience in a town called Ballybunion – a place with a much admired golf course. I had been kept awake late with a commotion outside in the street that sounded like a mob practicing yelling every foul word they knew.

I got out of bed a grouchy man. Our car was parked in the little central parking area in the middle of town, a short walk from the hotel. When I walked to get it, I noticed most of the shopkeeper's standing in their doorways. They seemed to be keeping an eye on me. When I got to the rented Volvo I knew why. The car had been vandalized – trashed – windshield wipers torn off, side view mirrors smashed and the car and its occupants had been thoroughly demeaned with curses scratched into the paint all over the surface.

I walked back to the hotel in a fury. Midway down the street I stopped and looked round at the shopkeepers who had now stepped from their doorways and were watching me closely and making no attempt at disguising their scrutiny. Standing in the middle of the street I shouted at them, "I'm sure some of you people know who did this. I'm going to the garda (police) now and report it. I hope you have the guts to give them some names." The good folks of Ballybunion lowered their glances, turned and went back into their shops.

The local garda officer shrugged when we walked in his office near the hotel and told him our story.

"Ahh, too bad but twasn't locals. I can tell you that," he said. I asked him who was on duty during the uproar last night. "No one," he said.

I asked him if he wanted to take a look at the car, though I realized it was pointless. No, he couldn't leave the office right now. He said there was a garage across the street but it wouldn't be open 'til later.

I started to speak and my wife knew the signs of my anger. She suggested I go get the car while she and the Murphys talked with the policeman.

When I returned they had somehow convinced him to call the garageman and ask him to come in and give us a hand.

The mechanic was only able to work a very makeshift windshield wiper on the driver's side, while he clucked about the vandalism done to the car: "A terrible, terrible thing but I can tell you one thing sure – twasn't locals."

It was sluicing rain when we left. The wiper fell off after a mile or so. The long trip to Killarney was made in the rain with the driver's window open while I leaned out and used the piece of metal with a handkerchief tied on to occasionally try to brush the water off the windshield.

We stopped in Killarney where a pleasant, ruddy-faced man worked out a windshield wiper for us. He frowned when we ended our Ballybunion story with "Of course, twasn't locals."

The rain stopped in Killarney and we savored the beauty of the lakes, the green lonely mountains being nuzzled by roaming sheep.

We came down out of the Connor Pass and the village of Dingle was in front of us, bravely defying the ocean at its face. For those of you who would like to know what Nantucket was like forty years ago, go to Dingle – but hurry.

A small cozy hotel named Benners is owned by some Americans we know. It is right in the heart of the little town just down the hill from the splendid and dramatically reconstructed Catholic Church with its base and upper walls of ancient weathered stone and soaring roof and dome of copper sheeting. I always mentally congratulate the unknown architect who brilliantly saved that church and the bishop who had the guts to approve the concept.

We checked into Benners. Polly and I had a comfortable room at the top of the stairs on the second floor. When I stowed our bags we all had a leisurely pint in the homey hotel pub that looks out onto the street. The events of the day gave us plenty to talk about. The four of us then slowly walked about the town. After a visit to the church we went across the street to a wonderful, better-than-first class restaurant called Begin Ish and made reservations for dinner.

To measure the dramatic change that occurred in the well named Emerald Isle in a generation, I offer you the restaurants of the country as a yardstick. Rough, unimaginative, quantity cooking has been replaced even in an out-of-the-way village like Dingle with food that would charm the most demanding trencherman.

A couple more pub stops and we were back at Benners to relax and get ready for dinner. Our bedroom window looked out on a flat tin roof. It had begun raining again and the sound of rain on the roof reminded me of my childhood. In fact, Dingle reminded me of long gone days. Many of our friends and neighbors had come from this town. I'd heard the name all my life and it always gave me a sense of fulfillment and in some strange way, achievement when I visited. The names on the shops and the pubs, the distinctive voices of the people were very familiar and carried me on a warm, sentimental journey home.

Dinner was superb and the bottles of wine we shared with it made for a night to remember. Astonishing really that we could eat and drink in such style in a little town that is located in what the Irish call "the back of the beyond."

There was still a thin rain as we walked down the hill to Benners. A night cap was certainly in order. I used to love to drink stingers on the rocks. I ordered one. Polly and Jim Murphy had some wine and "Rosie" Murphy had a stinger with me – one by one my pals went up to bed. I sat enjoying the chatter of the pub.

I decided to go for a late walk around the town but when I opened Benner's front door it was pouring, a hard wind-driven rain that came at you at an angle. I closed the door and went up the stairs to bed. I think I fell asleep before I closed my eyes.

Polly's elbow in my ribs woke me. Her mouth was near my ear. "There's somebody in the room," she said. I looked up and there was a man standing by the foot of the bed. I could make out his features from a faint light that came in the window. Above average height. Rain soaked dark curly hair. In less than the time I just took to write this, I was out of bed and at him.

Through the years when I have told this story some people have asked, *Why*? If you think about the situation for a moment you'll know why. There are no options.

The fellow was wet and slippery. I had trouble getting and keeping my hands around his neck and as we struggled I saw another figure in a jacket of sheep's wool – the wool side out – climbing in the window. Oh God, I thought, I can probably handle this guy, but two is going to be big trouble. I tried to knee my man in the crotch. We fell to the floor. Things were crashing. The man rolled away, got up and he was out the window in a flash, the sheep man ahead of him.

I pulled on some trousers and shouted to Polly, "Call 911!" – which doesn't exist in Ireland.

I raced downstairs. No one was at the front desk. The pub was crowded with its Saturday night crowd. It was near two o'clock. I yelled to the bartender, "Call the Garda. Two guys just broke into our room."

The pub went still and the bartender hustled from his station, saying, "The phone's at the reception desk."

An old timer called out from his seat by the window, "Two fellows just ran out from the alleyway and headed up the hill."

"Get the cops," I said firmly to the bartender. "I can identify those guys."

The young man went to the phone. I went out into the rain and ran up the hill in the sluicing water. There was a gritty pub at the top of the street and I had a thought that they might nip in there. I went into the pub. Three or four men stopped talking and watched me closely when I looked around the place. There was no late night lightheartedness here, although they had reason to be wary of a soaked, breathless stranger coming in out of the rain wearing a skivy shirt, slacks and loafers. The would-be robbers were not there.

There was a small crowd around the front desk at Brenners. Polly had put on slacks and a shirt and was sitting on the stairs. The door to the pub was ajar so that no one would miss a beat of this drum.

"Are they on the way?" I asked

"No."

"What do you mean, no?"

"Well, the Garda station closes at about six."

"It closes – the police station closes?"

"It does. Sergeant O'Donnell is in charge here, so I been tinkin' about callin' his house."

"You've been thinking about it. For God's sake, those guys haven't gotten far. I can identify them. Call his house."

"Aw, well his wife – she's, well . . . "

"C'mon call him. We can catch those guys."

The man slowly dialed a few numbers. He held the phone like a grenade with the pin pulled. After a bit he held the phone further from his ear and we could hear a barking voice. The young fellow got into his story of the break-in of the Yanks' room at Brenners when he was interrupted by more barking and then a dead phone.

"She hung up," he said to no one in particular. "O'Donnell's asleep. She doesn't want him bothered."

"Whyn't ye call her back?" someone behind me said. This got a fine reaction of chuckles and low guffaws from the gang in the lobby and as the story moved into the pub I could hear laughter.

"Where's the nearest open Garda station?" I snapped.

"Ahh, that would be Killarney, I think . . . "

The lobby group debated this for a bit and decided yes, Killarney it was.

"*Killarney*," I said, "you might as well call Chicago."

"Well," the clerk said, "she'll surely tell him in the mornin'."

A tiny wrinkled old timer with only a few wisps of grey hair and fewer teeth moved close to me and looked up with red-rimmed eyes. "Sure, you're wastin' your time, Yank."

"What do you mean?"

"You'll never be seein' them two again around Dingle."

"Why is that?"

"I'll tell you why, sir, because twasn't locals doin' a thing like that. Ahhh, no, twasn't locals."

I heard the murmurs of assent around me – the clerk was nodding his head in firm agreement.

The phone rang to wake us. Sunshine coming in the window gave us a good look at the shambles around us. The drapes had been torn down, a bureau was knocked on its side and a mirror was cock-eyed on the wall. When we got back to the room, I had merely righted a lamp and chair and we had then fallen into an exhausted sleep.

The call was from the front desk telling us that Sergeant O'Donnell was in the lobby and would like us to come down. I looked at my watch. It was ten thirty.

Polly jumped into jeans and a sweatshirt and hurried to the door.

I announced I was going to take a shower. Polly shook her head, "Please," she said.

"Hey, we waited for him, he can wait for us. It's midmorning now."

"Well, I'm going down, please hurry."

I was boiling with anger by the time I sauntered down the stairs to the lobby. Polly was sitting in an armchair watching a tall, thick-set, ruddy-faced man with an unruly thatch of greying black hair. He was wearing his navy blue Sunday morning Mass suit. He stopped pacing and rubbing his thick hands when Polly got up and met me at the foot of the stairs.

"Jack, this is Sergeant O'Donnell."

Neither one of us offered a hand.

"It was nice of you to rush over here, Sergeant. I'm really impressed."

That was how we opened. Our words got hotter and hotter and rather quickly we were circling one another. I noticed a young man and woman working the front desk standing stock still with wide eyes. They probably thought they were going to witness a historic battle. I thought so too and at the moment that was alright with me.

Fortunately for me, my wise wife stepped in between us. "Why don't we go up and look at the scene of the crime?" she said brightly, and that was bright for a couple of reasons. One being that Sergeant O'Donnell would have flattened me in three shakes of a lamb's tail, as the Irish say.

We walked into the bedroom and stood motionless. Polly and I studied O'Donnell as he studied the room. He turned to us and in his thick west of Ireland brogue said, "Now, don't touch a ting here, now."

I laughed out loud.

"For God's sake, Sergeant, this happened eight hours ago. My wife and I have been using the room since the break in."

"Ahh, sure," he said, "but anyway, they're well gone from Dingle."

"What makes you say that, Sergeant?" I asked.

"I say that because I can tell you this: twasn't locals that did this, no sir, twasn't locals."

## Afterwards

When we got home I wrote a letter to the *Irish Times* recounting our experiences. My letter was published at a moment when the country's policing was under a political microscope. My report caused an uproar in the country and became the focus of bitter debate in the Dail – the parliament of the Irish Republic.

I was called and agreed to an interview with Irish National Radio. At the end of very aggressive questioning, the interviewer clearly thought it was the Yanks' fault that someone broke into their room and positively averred that all the bad language in Ireland came from American influence ... we were offered free tickets to Ireland and accommodations throughout the country. I said "Thanks, but no thanks."

The bold interlocutor asked if that meant we would never visits Ireland again. "No," I said, "we hope to go back again."

Two years later we did go back. The same crew – Murphys and Warners – and we spent a night in Benners. No one said a word to us about our last visit. Not a look or a comment indicated anyone knew of the break in, the letter to the *Times* or the political uproar about policing.

Jim Murphy was delighted; he had repeatedly said no one would remember who we were. "Jim," I said, "I guarantee you that the drama of our last visit has been talked about endlessly all over the West of Ireland and will be for another ten years."

We were checking out of Benners – the Murphy's first – Jim paid his bill, said goodbye to the folks behind the desk. "That's it," he said and grinned at me triumphantly. Obviously no one remembered us. As I moved to step up to the desk, I noticed the bartender and waitress come out of the bar. The patrons followed. I paid our bill. The manager came out, seeming to check my bill. He looked up with the edge of a grin. "I wonder, Mr. Warner, will ye be stoppin' to see your friend Sergeant O'Donnell before ye leave Dingle?"

# Twenty Thousand People
# in the World

About five years after our adventures with the robbers in Benner's Hotel and the tardy Sergeant O'Donnell, our pal Betty Nolan was driving from Tralee to Dingle. She stopped at a lonesome little gift shop on a mountain top in an area known as Slieve Mish. Knowing Betty, she probably stopped because she wanted to give the owners a bit of much needed business.

Betty browsed through the shop for some minutes with no one in attendance. Finally an old man shuffled out in his slippers. He did not speak, but watched Betty with watery, wary eyes. After some more time spent in picking up pieces of this and that from the sparse inventory, Betty asked a question. The man brightened.

"Where are ye from?"

"I was born in Connemara."

"By God, I thought ye were a Yank."

Betty laughed and told him she lived in America. The end result of further chatter was an invitation to have a cup of tea in the Spartan living quarters in the back of the shop. The old man was a widower, watching the clock run down from his lonesome perch with his pipe and his dog. Betty could see chickens and rabbits outside the window in their pens.

He was clearly delighted to have Betty's company. Their discussion was wide ranging and soon the theme was how the world, especially the Irish world, had changed. "By God," the old man said, "weren't there two Yanks near killed in their beds in Dingle not long ago." Betty knew our story and was immediately alert, thinking not again.

"What happened?" she asked.

"Ah, a Yank and his wife, asleep in their bed in Benners – right

73

in the middle of the town – they were near killed – there was an awful fight. These blaguards came in the window in the middle of the night. Twas a terrible thing."

Betty was shaking her head with sympathy and wondering. "Did they catch them?"

"Ah, no. The Guarda couldn't come 'til morning. Sergeant O'Donnell it was. And then he and the Yank squared off right there in the front room there in Benners. A terrible thing altogether."

"What was that about?"

"Ach, I don't know. You know how some of those Yanks are."

Betty was smiling in spite of herself. "Did this happen four or five years ago?"

"Well, I suppose it was that long."

"And they never caught them?"

"Ah, no, how could they?"

"What do you mean?"

"Well, those fellows would be long gone from Dingle. They wouldn't be locals doin' a ting like that. Ah, no, twasn't locals."

# An Irish Christmas

If you've stayed with me on these stories, you've probably picked up on the fact that I like the Irish and am proud of my Irish heritage. My trips to Ireland have never been boring. One of my favorites – a Christmas trip in 1980.

My father died in 1979. A few years before his death, he and I traveled to Ireland. We spent time with our cousins who still live in the same farmhouse where his mother was born and raised. The farm occupies sweet, green land defined by ageless stone walls that march down along a sweep of sloping land that ends on the beach of Dunmanus Bay on the southwest tip of Ireland. It is a priceless place. But Ireland has many priceless places, and one of them is a village called Adare.

If you've flown into Shannon Airport and headed south, you have very probably raced right through Adare. It's about an hour south of the airport and my guess is that most people, still rubbing their eyes from a restless attempt to sleep through the short night on the trip from Boston or New York, whiz past the thatched-roof cottages and the low-roofed building with the modest sign that announces "The Dunraven Arms."

Those of us who know the place can tell you that you missed a jewel.

My Dad and I stopped at the Dunraven on our way south. I have a strange masculine memory of standing beside him in the cool of the dark green men's room, taking a shoulder-to-shoulder leak into the heavy, wall-length, yellowing tile urinal, thinking to myself, Here we are, men together. I hoped that some day I would stand like this with my own sons.

Less than a year from then, my father was gone.

I thought it would be a grand idea to take the family to Ireland for that Christmas, which was my father's birthday, and stay at the Dunraven.

My mother was thrilled. Her parents came from Ireland. They died when my mother was young, leaving her an orphan with dreams of a perfect green island across the sea that she had never seen, where life was slow and loving and musical. She yearned to visit Ireland. Christmas in Ireland with her family around her would be a dream come true.

To make the event even sweeter and more authentic, Dr. Colm and Brigid, an Irish couple who now lived in America and were dear friends of ours, decided to join us with their children. They also invited an assortment of their Irish families to book into the Dunraven for what was shaping up to be a very merry Christmas.

My mother dreaded flying. She almost wore out her rosary beads on the flight from Boston to Shannon. It was mid-morning by the time we were checked into the Dunraven.

About one hundred yards down the road from the inn there is a truly splendid stone church; its turreted tower dominates the town in a lordly yet protective manner. The church is unspoiled and goes back to the 15th Century. It must be one of the few Catholic churches in Ireland that escaped the unholy religious wrath of Oliver Cromwell.

No sooner had my mother come downstairs from unpacking in her "lovely" room, than she asked me to walk down the street with her to the church.

The interior of the church was stunning in its ancient simplicity – stone and oak. Our footsteps echoed somberly in its quietude. The mingled smell of hundreds of years of burning beeswax candles and incense had created an everlasting solemn perfume. We each lit a candle and knelt and prayed. A priest came in and was fussing with things on the altar. My mother got up, disdaining my helping hand – she was in her 80's then – and went over to speak to the priest. Their conversation rumbled off the stone walls. I paid no heed. Soon I rose to go over to her. She waved me off and indicated she'd meet me outside the church.

When we returned to the inn, Brigid and Colm and their children were in the lobby greeting members of their clan who had come from across Ireland to be with us to celebrate the holidays. We quickly adjourned to the homey, comfortable low-ceilinged lounge, which, as I recall, had a half dozen short-backed chairs facing a curved bar. The room was scattered with over-stuffed, well-used armchairs and low tables bearing fresh-cut flowers from the lush garden which bloomed outside the large paneled windows of the room. The garden and especially its stunning roses were a testimony to Ireland's benign and moist winters. But just in case, on one wall a fireplace, glowing with a peat fire, kept out any chill.

There was another tiny replica of this room further down the corridor. The Irish called it a "snug" or a "cozy" – it was well named. I would learn of this later. The central lounge was the stage on which our pal Brigid would perform during the two weeks we would spend at the Dunraven. Let me see if I can do her justice with my pen. Short, stocky – a fine looking woman whose blondish hair was usually cut short. She was the mother of four fine children, but that was not her primary occupation. Her main activity was being Brigid, full of movement, gossip – and, oh, well – here are some words that are part of her presence: boisterous, profane, chatter, laughter, stubbornness, all-knowing, with a heart as big as Ireland. Brigid was a member of the famous Dublin political Byrne family. She must have been hell on the male politicians in that family because I've never seen her take a backseat in any conversational vehicle.

So, as it was noontime, I asked the barman if it would be possible for us to have sandwiches and soup at the bar. "Of course it is," Brigid announced, and proceeded to prove it by ordering an array of thick, tasty sandwiches and a tray with a superb slab of smoked wild Irish salmon. Right about then I realized that the crowd was missing a spry, straight-backed eighty-something-year-old woman. As though on cue, my mother sailed past the door followed by two priests.

"Oh my God," Brigid exclaimed. "The priests have got hold of your mother already."

I went out and down the corridor to the snug where I found my mother with a tall, ruddy-faced, white-thatched monsignor and a slim young curate sitting comfortably by the fire. You'd have thought they'd known one another for years.

My mother gave me a rather arch look. She introduced me and then added, "I thought it would be nice to have these fine men come in and have a bite to eat. They suggested this little room. Isn't it lovely?"

That was a week before Christmas. For the days following, my mother entertained the monsignor and one and sometimes both of the curates.

The entertainment took the form of four o'clock tea. And what a tea. Thick creamy pastries, tarts, and fat-frosted cakes. I was not invited to these events. No one else was – not even my children who were each, in a special way, my mother's favorite. The teas, I learned – from Brigid, of course, who poked her nose in the snug whenever she felt like it – always ended with a couple of snifters of expensive brandy. My mother never drank, but in this case, Brigid reported, she always urged the "fine men" to "have one more."

It was Brigid who braced me in the lounge a few days before Christmas. She and her mother came in and sat on either side of me, both looking grim. "Jack," she said, and all business she was, "you've got to talk to your mother."

"About what?"

"This business with these priests."

"What business are you talking about?"

"This entertaining these priests – teas, cakes, brandy. My God, they'll bankrupt her –or you!"

"Hey, if she wants to do this, enjoys their company, I'm delighted."

"Jack, you know, you can be an awful asshole."

Her mother gave a little gasp. "You've mentioned that before Bridgetto," I said.

"Well, you are. Don't you know what she's doing?"

"What are you getting at?"

"A Mass on Christmas Day. She wants a Mass on Christmas Day said for your father."

"She does," affirmed her mother softly.

"That's what she's after, the poor woman." Brigid shook her head as she spoke.

"That will be wonderful," I said. "His birthday – here in Ireland – wonderful."

"Well, it won't happen," Brigid snapped.

"Oh, no, never," her mother said mournfully.

"Why won't it?"

"Because it won't. This is Ireland, not America. There's ways of doin' things here and on Christmas Day in Ireland no one – I mean no one – can have a Mass said for anyone. It's not done. It's not allowed. You've got to speak to your mother – those priests are leading her down the garden path, aren't they, Ma?"

"I'm afraid they are. You'd better talk to your mother, Jack, before she gets her poor heart broken."

"You're telling me that it's not allowed to offer a Mass for anyone, anywhere in Ireland on Christmas?"

"I am telling you that, and my mother is telling you that, and everybody else in this country will be telling you the same thing, smart ass. So talk to your mother and save her this grief. These priests won't – can't – remember your father in a Mass on Christmas Day. It is not done in this country. They are taking her for a nice tea and brandy ride every day."

Before tea time that afternoon, I had a talk with my mother. I planned to be as circumspect as possible. After a couple of words, my mother interrupted. "Brigid and her mother have been talking to you."

"Yes, they have."

I wouldn't mention that the entire Irish congregation was now discussing this matter as the first order of business. They were unanimously offended by the priests taking advantage of my "poor" mother. I spoke gently to her. "You know, Mom, it would be

79

wonderful to have a Mass said for Dad on Christmas, but it sounds as though things in the church here are different than they are at home. Don't get your hopes too high."

"Jack," (oh, oh, a bad sign), "are you having a good time here?"

"Wonderful, I hope everyone is."

"Well, I'm having the time of my life. This is the most wonderful Christmas present I've ever had. I love this place, I love these people, and that includes these fine men that spend their lives doing for others. Too many Catholics begrudge their priests a new pair of shoes. Don't you be one of them, and don't you worry about my hopes."

The teas continued. So did Brigid's exasperation and her mother's sorrowful head shaking.

Christmas Day was gray, overcast, damp, and mild. You knew you were a long way from New England.

Under my mother's sergeant-major's eye, the entire American-Irish-American-and Irish group of Warners and O'Riordans and their relatives assembled in the lobby of the Dunraven in the morning, everyone polished and primped for Christmas Mass.

The genial house manager, who was completely captivated by her, whispered to me, that the sergeant-major had been waiting with her hat and coat on for at least half an hour before anyone appeared. I smiled, but didn't bother to tell him that that's the way it had been at our house – forever.

With my mother out in front, with her arm in mine, our group strolled down the street to the church. There must have been twenty of us in all. We were quite early. My mother marched us down the middle aisle to the front pew. Our family took up that space. Right behind us were Colm, Brigid and their children.

The celebration of Christmas Mass in the ancient stone church in the village of Adare was pure and simple. The colors of the day were blood red and unsullied white. They were stark and stunning within the grey stone and worn oak interior of the church. Altar boys filed in, each wearing a white linen sleeveless alb beneath which was a long-sleeved red jersey. Each youngster carried a tall wooden candleholder on which was affixed a long white taper that danced with light. Every young man in the village and the farms surrounding must have been included in this group. They lined both sides of the main aisle and extended to each side of the simple stone altar.

After they had taken their places, a file of young girls and women, similarly dressed in white and red, entered the church from a side entrance and positioned themselves in a semi-circle on one side of the altar. An unseen organist began to play softly, and the choir commenced, their voices captured sweet and clear by the stone walls and slate roof.

The monsignor entered from the back of the church and was preceded down the middle aisle by the two curates, each carrying a plain wooden cross. They were also dressed in white and red. In the midst of this, the mundane thought came to me of the hours of scrubbing and ironing that must have been done by the women of the parish to present these crisp, pure linen offerings to the Lord on Christmas Day.

Monsignor knelt before the altar, then rose and turned to the congregation. "Today's Mass will be said in the Irish language," he announced in strong, yet musical voice.

The celebration of the Mass proceeded and as the strange words and phrases flowed over me, my thoughts drifted to days and places a long way off. The cadence and twists of the Gaelic mesmerized me.

When the Monsignor climbed the curved stairway to the pulpit, I watched as from a great distance. The foreign sounds of his homily massaged my spirit.

Suddenly I was jolted back to Adare. English words came from the Monsignor as he looked down at the worshipers: "Today's Mass is offered in memory of Leonard Warner of America."

The church was completely silent and into that silence burst the exclamation of Brigid O'Riordan, her words ricocheted off the ancient walls, "Well, I'll be a son of a bitch."

# Family Reunion

I've known a few people who could qualify to fit the role, or the public's perception of the role of a "Boston Pol." None stands out as vividly as the late Patrick J. "Sonny" McDonough. Describing Sonny, a thesaurus would come in handy. His character contained a complex mix of conflicting traits. He could be warm, sentimental, cruel, boisterous, gentle, caring, generous, grasping, friendly, or cold. Overriding all of these impulses, however, was the charm and wit of the brilliant Irish storyteller – the *shanachie* of Gaelic history.

Sonny came from South Boston. He was an elected state official in various capacities for years and years. From his perch in these jobs, he sold insurance to one and all, and that certainly included folks interested in political appointments. He was investigated more often than he had birthdays. He was never found guilty of anything.

His power in Southie was such that, though he represented the district in various positions for, I guess, well over thirty years, for a good part of his life he spent about half the year on his boat down on Marathon Island in the Florida Keys.

It was on Sonny's boat one day that he told me this story.

In the late 1920's, prohibition was making a lot of people rich – including young Patrick J. "Sonny" McDonough. A big shiny Packard, tailor made suits, and a bowler hat announced to Southie and the world that Sonny was a success. There was no one he wanted to impress more than his father, Pat. His dad was an immigrant who had come from a little village outside of Galway in the west of Ireland. His father almost never spoke of his youth or the old country. But for Sonny, his Irishness was the pride of his life. So years of incessant prodding of his father elicited some

82

vital scraps of information: the name of the village, the names of the brothers who worked the farm. Sonny cherished every piece of information and shared it with his admirers.

With his wallet and pride bursting, Sonny decided that he and his father would make a triumphant visit to the old homestead. "We'll go back to Ireland, Pa, you and I. We'll go see the family. We'll go first class all the way." To his surprise, his father gave him a short, sharp, "No." He'd had enough of Ireland and was never going back. And as far as he was concerned the subject was closed.

Weeks of cajoling were useless. And if Sonny McDonough couldn't talk somebody into something, nobody could. The old man was not going back.

"Well, the hell with you then. I'll go myself," Sonny decided. And so Sonny went back to the land of his pride and dreams.

He stayed in the best hotel in Galway. He hired a driver and the biggest car he could find to take him out to his father's village.

The sight of the big car with Sonny sitting in the back with his homburg hat tilted, his impeccable pin-stripe suite and silk tie seemed to strike the locals in the village speechless. Finally the lordly American got directions to the McDonough homestead. He got out of the car and strode into the yard of the raggedy, thatched-roof cottage. Three dirty-faced children of undetermined ages were playing by a pile of turf. They stared at him now in stock-still silent wonder. After repeating his question three or four times as to where he could find Michael McDonough, one of the children walked around the house and, still silent, pointed to a field where a man was wrestling a plow being pulled by a massive horse. Sonny tip-toed across the fresh-turned clods of earth, trying hard to keep his shiny shoes and spats clean.

The man with the plow never stopped and Sonny walked along beside him with his special South Boston smile on his face, announcing that he was his brother Pat's son: "I'm your nephew from America, " he announced grandly, as he tried to elude the flipping bits of earth from the plow. The man continued to plow and glared at him. Sonny repeated the announcement: "I'm Pat's' son, I'm Patrick Junior, your nephew from America. I've come here to see you. I'd like to meet the family."

Still not speaking, Sonny's uncle, yanked the horse to a stop. He turned and headed back to the house, with Sonny tripping along beside him. In the low-ceilinged kitchen of the cottage, with chickens running in and out of the open door, Sonny stood while the man stared at him until Sonny, himself, announced to the once handsome woman by the stove who he was and that he had come from America to meet the family and bring his father's best wishes.

Suddenly, for the first time, his uncle, Michael, spoke. "What is it you want of us?"

Never stuck for an answer, Sonny announced that he would like to take the whole family into Galway for dinner the next day. It was clear that a trip to Galway was beyond the imagination of anybody in the room. However, Sonny dealt with that in his usual efficient, imperious manner, and said he would have a car out there the next day to pick up the family and they would have a great celebratory supper at the Great Southern Hotel. There were no hugs, no kisses, not even a handshake from his uncle Michael, and a somewhat puzzled Sonny headed back to Galway.

Sonny decided that a master stroke was needed to save this reunion. When the family assembled, nervous, smelling of soap, in the lobby of the hotel the next evening, he announced that he had placed a telephone call to his father in America. This itself was a miraculous event in 1920's Ireland. The family assembled in a small room off the lobby and stood in rigid anticipation, staring at the telephone on the table. The manager of the hotel came in and announced to Sonny that the connection had been made. The United States was on the line.

Sonny took the phone and announced to his father that he was standing in the Great Southern Hotel in Galway with his brother Michael and Michael's family by his side, and they wanted to say "hello" to him.

The next sound that Sonny McDonough heard seemed to be moaning and crying and he wondered if the connection had gone bad. He finally realized that he was, for the first time in his life, hearing the sound of his father crying.

"Ask them to forgive me."

Oh, God.

"Ask them to forgive me...God forgive me!"

There was a sound of further crying and sobbing and the line went dead.

Sonny looked at his uncle Michael. "My father was crying," he said. "He asked you to forgive him."

Uncle Michael looked hard at his nephew. "Your father had the job of herding our best heifers and a bull to the auction in Galway – he took them in one summer morning. We never saw him again."

# Politics is Personal

*Hon. Robert Q. Crane*

# Spending Some Time
# with Harry Truman

One of my father's best friends and, I'm sure, a personal hero, was named Tom Moriarty. Tom was the District Attorney for Western Massachusetts. He looked like he was born for, at least, that job. In fact, he had turned down opportunities to run for Governor, Congress and the Senate. He was the D. A. and he was going to stay the D. A.

Tom was a bit over six feet with military posture. (He had been an officer in the First World War). He had narrow hips and very wide shoulders above which was a large leonine head of silver hair. Tom had been an outstanding football player at Georgetown back in the days when they were a national power.

He always looked to me as though he could still play. He was a man's man if there ever was one. He never married, probably because he had too many choices. My recollection is of a beautiful wealthy widow who was his longtime friend.

Tom's presence and brains and authority made him a political power across the state and beyond. He was a Franklin D. Roosevelt Democrat. He was campaign manager for Massachusetts' most powerful Democrat, Paul Dever, who was Attorney General for years and two-term Governor. He had roomed in law school with Frank Murphy who became Governor of Michigan and was appointed a justice of the Supreme Court by Roosevelt. They had remained very close friends.

Tom had a long and very effective reach and he did his reaching from a modest farm where he and his brother lived in a small town outside Springfield called Wilbraham. His brother ran the farm and Tom Moriarty, the D. A., ran a great many other things and people.

I had just gotten out of the Marine Corps and was back in Westfield. My father asked me if I would like to accompany him and the D. A. to Boston to the annual big – really big – state Democratic affair, fund raiser, pat-ourselves-on-the-back evening that was entitled the Jefferson/Jackson Day Dinner. I couldn't say *Yes* fast enough. I was hooked on politics and to be at such an event in the company of Tom Moriarty should be a memorable experience.

We went to Boston in Tom's big car. He had a plainclothes state cop as a driver. As I remember, if Tom took one drink at our house or any place away from the farm, he would go to the phone and have a driver sent to him.

On our way to Boston we were the lead car in a caravan of cars full of politicians of all sizes and shapes from all over what was always called "Western Mass," all following their leader, the D. A.

In the car on the way, Tom mentioned that the speakers at the dinner would be quite a trio: President Harry Truman, who was now former President Harry Truman; another former, James Michael Curley, who was former Mayor of Boston, Congressman, Governor and jailbird, who had been pardoned by Truman; and the young congressman from Boston, Jack Kennedy. Quite a trio indeed.

The Western Mass gang had a large section of tables in the big Statler Hotel ballroom. Tom did me the honor of asking me to sit beside him, "so we can talk." The other ten seats at our table were occupied by my dad and judges, some of whom got into the liquid refreshments in a big way. At one point one of them stood and offered a wavering toast to Tom, "Here we all are" he said, "judges by the grace of Tom Moriarty."

"Sit down, Joe and take it easy," Tom told him quietly, but very firmly.

I don't remember much about the speeches. Kennedy looked very young. He was very thin and there was an air of fragility about him. There was a lot of buzzing about him and Curley at the same table. The Kennedys had made a public point of John F. Kennedy not joining in with the Massachusetts Congressional Delegation in petitioning President Truman to release James Michael from prison early – which Truman had done.

I do remember that when Curley spoke he quoted Oliver Goldsmith, which many of the pols in attendance thought was a wondrous thing after they asked one another, "Who the hell is Oliver Goldsmith?" and eventually learned he was a long dead Irish author.

Jack Kennedy spoke briefly and humorously; he certainly did have a special quality that emanated through the big room.

After the speeches were concluded and Truman left, it looked to me as though there would be a real party. Tom Moriarty turned to me, "Would you like to meet President Truman, Jack?" he asked. I said I would love to. Harry Truman was one of my heroes.

We took an elevator to the top floor and when the door opened there were two big Boston cops standing shoulder to shoulder in front of us. One of them was shaking his head indicating we couldn't get off; the other quickly "made" Tom. "Hi ya, Mister D. A. Lemme go get the captain." The corridor behind them was jammed. A tall police captain was soon in front of us. Tom shook the extended hand and said, "Captain, would you see if President Truman has a minute to say hello to Tom Moriarty and a friend?"

While the captain went off, I surveyed the scene. Near us were perhaps a couple of dozen photographers. One was a small red headed fellow – he was busy cursing Truman. The red head was angry at wasting time to cover such a jerk, son of a bitch, half-assed, etc., etc. From the crowd beyond, three or four people were calling out to Tom, asking if he could get them in to see the President.

While the police captain is on his mission, let me give you some history of that moment. Truman was no longer President. Eisenhower had the job. There was real bitterness between the two men – some of it caused by what had been said about a man

90

who was Truman's hero and was the major architect of Eisenhower's career, General George Catlett Marshall.

Senator Joe McCarthy had vilified Marshall, going so low as to call him "a traitor." This of the man who stands unquestionably as one of America's great patriots. Marshall had taken Eisenhower from obscurity and made him a general and ultimately head of the allied forces in Europe. Marshall later became Secretary of State under Truman. He was the quintessential unselfish patriot.

Despite Marshall's known rectitude, Nixon chimed in with McCarthy's attack. Through all this, Eisenhower never spoke a public word to defend his mentor and chief. Truman was in the initial stage of a public battle defending Marshall and describing President Eisenhower as disloyal, ungrateful and living in fear of Senator McCarthy. This is one of the reasons that Statler Hotel lobby was jammed with press people and photographers.

The other historical fact involves me in a rather peripheral way. During the Korean War – I think it might have been just after the First Marine Division was trapped up at the Choisin Reservoir by the Chinese Armies – Harry Truman, President, Commander in Chief, and also, very much World War I Army combat vet, made a crack that "the Marine Corps gets more publicity than Hollywood. It's got a better propaganda machine than Joe Stalin." Well, as you can imagine, Marines, ex-Marines, their families, Truman haters, everybody that could work their way in, got in line to give Truman a kick.

The President handled this in typical Truman style. The Marine Corps was having a reunion in Washington, in a hotel down the street from the White House. Truman was definitely not invited. When the ballroom was full for the opening ceremony, Harry put on his fedora and walked down the street into the hotel and up on the stage. He apologized to the Marine Corps and brought down the house. Some Marines wanted to carry him back to the White House on their shoulders.

So here we are back in the jam-packed corridor of the Statler Hotel and the rangy police captain has just returned. "Follow me, please, Mister D. A. They said the President wants you to come right in." Tom put me in front of him and we ploughed through the crowd with the cops running interference.

I found myself standing in front of a door. One of the cops knocked. The door was opened by Harry S. Truman. He looked up at me. I looked down at him.

First impression: a small fellow – little guy – big head. Yes, a small fellow with an outsized head which was covered with a well combed thatch of greyish-white hair but it was the glasses that held my attention. Very thick, as thick as a prism but they did not obscure the large unblinking grey eyes which stared closely into my eyes for a moment and then seemed to check me out from head to toe with a sweeping glance. He then saw Tom behind me and reached past me and I stepped aside. I never thought of Truman as an affectionate guy, but he was at that moment. He put an arm up around Tom's shoulders and gave him an awkward hug.

"Tom, it's a treat for me to see you. Thank you for coming by."

"You look great, Mister President. It is a pleasure to be with you again. Excellent speech, by the way."

"Thanks, Tom. Now come on in here. I want to tell these folks about you."

"First, Mister President I'd like to introduce a friend of mine." Tom turned to me and gave me a very generous introduction, "Mister President, I'd like to introduce a friend of mine. This is Jack Warner, a captain in the Marines who's back home with us now."

I took Truman's outstretched hand and got what I expected: a strong, firm, manly shake.

"Captain Warner, " Truman said, "Glad to meet you."

"It's a pleasure to meet you, sir," I said.

And then Harry Truman gave me something I didn't expect, with a trace of a grin he asked, "Are you guys still sore at me?"

My face surely must have showed my surprise. When I

answered "No, no sir." he really grinned. Then he put his hand on Tom's shoulder and raised his voice as he and Tom moved into the center of the spacious living room.

"I want you folks to come and meet one of the best friends I ever had."

I stood in a corner of the appropriately named Presidential Suite and watched and listened, feeling like a schoolboy. There were perhaps a dozen people in the room. I was clearly the youngest.

"This is my friend Tom Moriarty." Truman was standing close to Tom with a hand upon his shoulder. "Tom has been my friend for a long time – long before I became President. Tom could have had any appointment within my power to give because he is as capable and smart and tough as anyone I know. But Tom decided to stay on his farm in Wilbraham (I was amazed that Truman could withdraw the town's name from his memory bank) and he's done that and still influenced many many things." Mister Truman turned to Tom and with a wide smile asked, "Do you remember when I called you – woke you up in the middle of the night – from Denver during the '48 campaign?"

Truman continued before Tom could responded so he nodded and matched Truman's smile as the former President talked on. "Well, we were stuck in Denver – President of the United States campaigning for election." Truman was clearly relishing telling his story. "The railroad people wouldn't move the train 'til they got paid. You can see who they thought was going to win that election. We were broke. They said they wouldn't give us credit. We planned to campaign in that train up and down the State of California and all over the west coast, but we couldn't get out of Denver Station. President of the United States, stuck in a train station – I called Tom in the middle of the night. He raised the money, took care of everything. The train left Denver in the morning." Truman looked up at Tom and beamed.

"You forgot to tell them that you won the election, Mr. President," Tom added. The group laughed as though on cue and gathered round the two men. I watched and listened, fascinated, from my place in the corner.

A while later, I noticed a man enter from a door at the far end of the room. He approached Truman and his group and spoke in a voice that seemed to signify that the socializing was over.

"The press is assembled and waiting, Mr. President."

Truman spoke briefly with some of his admirers and then turned from them and strode across the room. Well, I thought, that's it. I met Harry Truman, shook hands with him and have a nice little story of his asking if Marines "were still sore at him." What a night. What a nice memory.

Mr. Truman stopped in mid-stride, almost out the door. He looked around. "Where's that young Marine?" he asked.

I straightened up, came to attention in the corner. "Right here, Mr. President."

He beckoned to me and I went to him. "How would you like to sit in with me at this press conference? Give you a taste of what it's like."

I think I said, "I'd like that very much, sir." In fact all I can truthfully say is I responded positively because the next thing I knew I was walking into a good-sized room that had a winged chair in some open space in a corner and within four feet or so the room was crammed. It felt like floor to ceiling with people; the front two or three rows with photographers, many on one knee. The former President looked at the single chair and then around the room. As he did, the red-headed photographer who had been cursing Truman out in the corridor was fumbling with his equipment and dropped something. Truman walked over, bent down, and retrieved the object. Our eyes met for a moment and the man had the decency to flush the color of his hair as Harry Truman handed him the piece.

Truman then turned to me and said, "We've got to get you a chair." With that said, he spotted another winged chair behind a pack of reporters and quickly walked through them and began to manhandle the chair. I was rather dazed following behind. The press crowd stared, bemused, no one moved to offer a hand. I reached him and put a hand on his arm. "Please don't do that Mr. President. I'll get it." I realized that moving the chair in that jam would be a project and I didn't want Harry Truman embarrassed by these people.

"You know, Mr. President, I can sit right on the floor beside your chair if that's all right."

"You don't mind doing that?"

"No, sir."

So I sat on the rug beside the chair of this thoughtful, kindly man.

When the first question came from the press, the air in the room changed at once and became charged with electricity. Truman's answers were clipped, hard, and commanding. No matter the subject – President Eisenhower, Vice President Nixon, Senator McCarthy, the press itself and General Marshall. I was amazed by the presence and power that emanated from the little man from Missouri who had been going to move furniture a few minutes before.

I sat there beside one of America's great historical personages in front of dozens of cameras and never had the presence of mind to ask one of those people to take a picture for me to save, but I've saved the memory.

# The Big Question

Politics is a very intense line of non-work. I don't think there is much humor in it now; at least there doesn't appear to be. But politics used to be funny.

When I was a member of Endicott "Chubb" Peabody's administration, it was decided to reorganize the Department of Public Works. This was one of the state's largest agencies. The department was in the midst of planning and overseeing the construction of the Interstate Highway System, the largest construction job and the biggest expenditure of money the state had ever known.

The DPW had been getting some bad press – a lot of it, in fact. A congressman from Minnesota named Blatnick had decided to use his congressional committee to investigate the Interstate program all over America – most especially in Massachusetts. The papers were front-paging daily rumors of alleged misdeeds in the highway program. But the fact was that no one as yet had been found guilty of anything. Nevertheless, the press had already decided that the villain was a DPW Commissioner named Jack Riccardi. Jack had never been proved guilty of anything, and never was, except perhaps having been born with the wrong last name. The newspapers in Boston were hammering Riccardi constantly and the governor for keeping him in his powerful job.

Reorganization of the DPW would be perhaps a not too subtle way of getting rid of Riccardi and getting the newspapers off the Governor's back. So with all the fairness that life is so loaded with, the state legislature, which liked Jack, was terrified into passing the reorganization bill when one of the other DPW commissioners was indicted by Attorney General Ed Brooke (later U. S. Senator) on a charge that made page one headlines all across the state. No matter that, months later, the indictment was thrown out. That news was a small paragraph on the back pages of newspapers.

So there was to be a new Public Works Commission. Governor Peabody decided I would be the key man in this new, improved Department of Public Works. My first job was to find some new people to serve as my fellow commissioners. Well qualified people across the state were being considered. Whoever the "picks" would be, it had to be fast. The political pot was boiling.

For reasons I can't recall, it was decided that I would interview the first possibility in the governor's office at 7:30 in the morning. The governor and a couple of his top aides would not be seen, but would be listening to the interview through a partially open door in the next room. Yes, this is wacky but that's what we did.

We'll call the applicant "Tony," because that happened to be his name. He showed up in what appeared to be a new blue suit. He was from a nearby city and I opened the conversation by mentioning mutual friends and politicians from his town. It was very hard to get more than nods and grunts out of him, even in this benign conversation. I continued with questions about his background, education, family, asked about his engineering degree, etc. which he answered as briefly as possible. When I was through with this, I said, "Well, Tony, I'm sure you have many questions about things at the Department of Public Works." He shook his head.

"Well, you're certainly aware of the constant front page stuff that's going on about the Interstate Highway System and payments on land takings and some of the problems that may exist down at the department.?" He shook his head. This was turning into one hell of an interview. I asked a couple of more questions but still got nothing but a shake of the head. Not interested.

Finally, with one eye on the partially opened door where the governor and his aides were listening, and I figured, perhaps as exasperated as I was, I said, "Well, Tony, you must have a question about this job."

"Well," he said, "I do."

*Finally*, I thought.

"What's your question, Tony?" I asked.

"What time do you have to get to work in the morning?"

I took a deep breath to keep from laughing, and said, "Tony, don't worry about that. We'll be in touch with you."

He went out one door and I went into the other door and said to the governor, "You heard that! We certainly can't use that guy."

"Too late," said the governor. "I've already made a deal. The Italians are in an uproar over getting rid of Riccardi, so we've got to announce an Italian today and it's gonna' be him."

# Political Appointment

A fellow named Lester Hyman was a very active liberal Democrat in Massachusetts. He was an aggressive, articulate lawyer who ran for the job of Attorney General of Massachusetts. Despite his tall good looks and hard work, he was buried by his Irish – what else? – opponent in the Democratic primary.

Lester decided that Massachusetts was too parochial for his ambition. He would move to Washington, practice law there and make his mark on the national scene. He had no trouble joining a good firm in D. C. and was soon up to the top of his wallet in national Democratic politics. He was helped by the fact that a neighbor in Washington was a charming Senator from Minnesota named Walter Mondale. Lester became very friendly with the Mondales. He was a frequent visitor to their house which was across the street from his apartment.

When a deceptively modest man from Georgia named Jimmy Carter decided to try the leap from governor to president, Lester and Senator Mondale decided to get on the trampoline with him at the beginning of the performance.

It was Lester's hope, a hope he shared with his friends, that a Carter victory would bring him the job of Attorney General of the United States. Lester and Senator Mondale worked long and hard for Jimmy Carter. Lester raised money, traveled the country, spent hours brainstorming with the senator and his allies in the Mondale kitchen.

When Carter won the Democratic nomination, Lester was ecstatic – Ah, what a world to be living in. The next day when Carter chose Mondale as his running mate, Lester Hyman was – what words will define his state? – ah, what a world to be sitting on top of!

When the resolution of the contest was decided on election

night – Carter the President, a man Lester knew personally, discussed policy with, and Mondale, Vice President, a man who was Lester's friend, no, pal , who he had entered the battle with, worked, toiled, planned, shared late night kitchen conferences with – ah, what a world to own. What a world to be Attorney General of!

Massachusetts political observers – of which there are approximately 2,650,000 – decided that Lester Hyman was the luckiest son of a bitch who ever lived. Massachusetts lawyers – of which there are approximately 1,725,000 – decided they had always liked, admired, and respected the legal genius of Lester Hyman and would be proud to serve in any federal job, especially judge or U. S Attorney, that the prospective Attorney General of the U. S. would offer them. Hundreds remembered they "voted for Lester" that time he ran for A. G..

Lester almost held his breath as the new president began to pick his cabinet – almost but not quite. He did confide in many of his friends – and he now had many friends – that he felt he was on the inside track to be Attorney General, the boss of the Department of Justice of the new administration. The tension built and reached maximum limits by a call from Vice President Mondale. "Could you stop by the house tomorrow night? There is something personal we should talk about."

The world stood still, except for the many top secret, off-the-record, calls that Lester made to his host of friends. Tomorrow night finally came. Lester Hyman and Vice President Walter Mondale sat once again in the kitchen having a drink. Lester on the edge of his chair, glass tightly held – early chitchat, catching up, so and so and this and that. Then Mondale said, "Lester, you know we'll be moving soon, into the Vice Presidential house at the Naval Observatory. We're leaving the neighborhood."

A measured nod and thoughtful and little sad, "Um humm" from Lester.

"So," said Mondale apologetically, "I'm afraid you'll have to take those frozen steaks that you keep here in the freezer."

That was it. Mondale had nothing to offer on Lester's hopes for the top spot at Justice. Lester took home the package of steaks. He threw them out the back window of his apartment.

# How Boston Got to Dig Big

Frank Sargent, who was once Governor of Massachusetts, served on the Massachusetts Public Works Commission with me. I was in charge of highways; Frank was in charge of waterways. We got to be very good friends. Frank got more mileage out of a hearty laugh and good humor than any person I ever met in my life. He was a very careful, cautious man, in particular when it came to things political. His antennae were always fine tuned for what the media wanted. A good press was always Frank's goal. He avoided controversy and controversial people like a spinster crossing the street at the approach of the town drunk.

While Frank was at the Department of Public Works, a major highway program was underway. We were planning and taking the property for a project that would relieve a major part of Boston's and its neighboring cities' constant traffic jams. It was called "the inner belt." It was a system of highways that worked like spokes coming off Boston's hub road, Route 128 and was designed to alleviate commuter tie-ups and push north-south traffic through Boston.

In those days, Tom Winship was the dynamic, all-powerful editor of the *Boston Globe.* He was a very charming, shrewd guy. To drop a name, I once told author David Halberstam that Winship was the most powerful and effective editor in America, and many times I have read Halberstam repeating my words. In fact, I believe those words were in Winship's obituary.

Tom Winship and the *Boston Globe* – and make no mistake, when he was editor, he **was** the *Boston Globe* – was a very liberal guy. He kept his paper and his people on target in favor of a liberal agenda – school busing was near the top of that list. Winship and his newspaper never wavered in supporting busing, even as the city, its people, and its schools were torn apart physically and psychologically. Winship believed busing was the right thing to do. I used to tell him it was easy to be in favor of busing when you lived out in Lincoln as he did. Or in – I think – Wellesley, where the judge who enforced the law lived. Tom would bristle and then chuckle. He was not a rancorous man, but he held strong opinions.

He once told me that supporting busing had cost the *Globe* nearly a 25,000 drop in city circulation.

Among one of Winship's strongest opinions was that building highways was a bad idea. Any highways, anywhere.

It came to pass that Frank Sargent became Governor of the Commonwealth of Massachusetts, and on one of the first days of his administration, he told me he was going to have lunch with Tom Winship at the Tavern Club, the last bastion of the Yankees in downtown Boston.

"Winship is going to want to talk highways with you," I told Frank. "Don't get suckered in. You know we've taken all the land for the first part of the inner belt, and the project will be a lifesaver for Boston. Don't let him talk you out of it. He's against road building, but take a stand on this, Frank. The inner belt will be a very positive help to the city and the suburbs. The anti-road people are wrong on this, don't let him turn you around."

Sargent nodded his agreement, gave me a big smile, and off he went.

At the end of the day, Frank, my pal Don Dwight, who was Lieutenant Governor, and I met for a drink. "How'd your luncheon go?" I asked.

The Governor looked very uneasy. "Well, Jack, you're right. Winship is dead against highways, and in particular the inner belt.

"So," I asked, unnecessarily. "What happened?"

"I'm afraid I told him we wouldn't build the inner belt."

Thus, from a luncheon with the editor of the *Globe* and the Governor came the decision that stopped highway building in Boston for almost thirty years, and created the circumstances for the largest, most expensive, and least rewarding construction project in American history called "The Big Dig."

# That's All the President Said?

One of the things that governors do in Massachusetts is appoint judges. The lawyers who receive these plums from the top of the career tree are judges for the rest of their lives. It is the dream of countless lawyers – maybe not all, but probably pretty close – to put on the black robe, have a courtroom of folks snap to their feet upon his or her honor's arrival, and be treated like deity in and out of the courtroom. Why not?

In Massachusetts lawyers are in the front lines of every gubernatorial campaign. If you could get your hands on a magic fluorescent lamp, you would be able to see the sign that lawyers can see imprinted on the candidate's forehead: "I can make you a judge."

In the once great city of Holyoke, Mass., there was a district judge named Nolan. Judge Nolan was a man of wisdom and compassion blended with deep respect for the law. He sat in judgement on the foibles of his city for many years. There is no more powerful position in any of our towns than Presiding Justice of the District Court.

In those days, district courts also had what were called "associate justices." They were part-time judges who filled in, took on overloads, did the extra work needed. They could continue to practice law in front of the presiding district judge. The associate justice in Holyoke was a very bright young man named George Beauregard.

Holyoke was an exciting, competitive town of ethnic mixes. There was a small Yankee group that controlled the banks, the newspaper and television. Then came the large Irish contingent. I knew people from Holyoke who spoke with the brogue of their parents and grandparents who had never been closer to Ireland than Worcester. Holyoke had a Polish and a French population, all proud and very active in city affairs. A small Jewish contingent kept a wary eye on everybody. The Westfield-Holyoke athletic rivalry was enduring and intense. One of my closest friends was first a rival – he had a long illustrious career as Holyoke High Football Coach. A marvelous American place was Holyoke.

George Beauregard was a young man the Franco-American Society was extremely proud of. When Irish Judge Nolan retired – and he'd been on the bench a long time – this brilliant young man of French descent was in line to take the position of high honor and power. The French community waited with prideful anticipation.

During the time I write of, another young man from Massachusetts had assumed a position of some honor and power. John F. Kennedy became a congressman.

One of Congressman Kennedy's objectives in working his way to the White House was to establish himself as a thoughtful observer of foreign affairs. To aid this goal, he somehow decided to focus on the savage civil war being fought in the French colony of Algeria. Kennedy in the House, and subsequently in the Senate, produced policy papers from his office and gave major speeches criticizing the French government and suggesting new paths to follow to find peace in Algeria. All of this took place in the 1950's.

Out in Holyoke, in western Massachusetts, George Beauregard, as president of the Franco-American Society and a practicing amateur historian, took issue with and criticized Kennedy's proposals. He made his argument in a number of letters to the local daily newspaper, the *Holyoke Transcript*.

In the early 1960's, it was my good fortune to be asked to be a member of the administration of a wonderful man who was elected governor named Endicott Peabody, nicknamed and known to one and all as "Chubb."

It was a strange thing about Chubb Peabody – he had as many or more credentials for glamour than anyone I've ever known. He was the grandson of the legendary Bishop Peabody who founded and held Groton Academy in his hands until his death as an old man. Chubb earned a national reputation as a fierce All-American football player at Harvard, just before World War II. In the second war, he won America's second highest medal for bravery in combat: the Navy Cross. He was a sub-mariner who led a boarding party onto a Japanese destroyer and captured it in hand-to-hand fighting. Yet glamour, or even celebrity never seemed to come to this fine man and his lovely wife. The newspapers were generally hostile to him, other pols cut him, his own lieutenant governor double-crossed him and ran against him.

The fact is that Massachusetts had room for only one human stellar system – their name was Kennedy.

In early 1962, Jack Kennedy was President and the Harvard football hero and contemporary of Jack's was Governor. There was an awkwardness between them that I sensed on the two or three occasions I heard the Governor speak with the President on the phone.

One day the Governor asked me and one of his legal aides if we'd like to take a ride out to the airport to greet the President who was coming in to spend a few days in Hyannisport.

On the drive over to Logan Airport in the Governor's big car with state police motorcycle outriders – there because this was a Presidential deal – the legal aide mentioned that Judge Nolan of Holyoke had died the day before. There would be a judgeship to be decided.

When we arrived at Logan, we drove right out onto the runway. There were columns of troops lined up – I think National Guard and Air Force. I saw my friend Charlie Sweeney – he was a brigadier in the Air Force at that time.

The President's plane was not as big as those monsters they use now. It glided in nicely and pulled up right by our car. Kennedy came off the plane as soon as the stairs were in place. The troops snapped to attention. The band played "Hail to the Chief." Here he was – the leader of the free world. I only saw John Kennedy three times in my life but each time I received the same mix of impressions. A skinny, handsome, vulnerable looking guy with immense self confidence. The complete master of every scene.

Chubb Peabody, who had every reason to feel the personal equal to the President, looked like an awkward supplicant in his rumpled raincoat as he welcomed the President.

I knew a couple of the players with the President and said hello to them: Kenny O'Donnell, always cocky, always with an eye on his boss, even as he made small talk; and Larry O'Brien, ever courteous and careful and thoughtful. A one-time bartender in his dad's saloon in Springfield, he was the pride of Western Massachusetts. He would prove invaluable to two presidents.

We watched the President and the Governor troop the lines and chat very briefly. I knew Peabody had a number of items on his agenda to talk with the President about, but they clearly weren't having anything like a conversation. O'Donnell mentioned the boss was in a hurry to get to the Cape.

Kennedy and Peabody shook hands briefly and as the President turned to leave the Governor gave him a fine hand salute which I found touching.

We got back in the car as the Presidential limousine roared off. They now had the state police outriders.

The Governor stared out the window saying nothing. The legal aide and I watched him closely. Finally, the aide spoke. "Do you mind if I ask, sir?"

Peabody shrugged.

"What did the President have to say?"

"He said he heard that Judge Nolan in Holyoke died, and asked who I had in mind for the job. I told him I hadn't decided yet." He paused

"And?" the aide asked

"And then he said, 'Don't give it to that prick Beauregard.'"

"That's all he said?" the aide asked.

"Yes, that's all the President said."

# Speaking of Presidents

Back in the late 60's and early 70's there was a short, intense, humorless son of Greek immigrants serving in the Massachusetts House of Representatives named Michael Dukakis.

Dukakis represented the edge of Boston town of Brookline. Brookline was and is a solid Democratic town. There are none more solidly liberal in the left wing Democratic Republic of Massachusetts, and Mike Dukakis led and controlled politics in Brookline and played the same role with the liberal, good government contingent in the Massachusetts House.

I was involved in politics at that time. I had spent some time on the State Public Works Commission and then accepted a high profile job from the mayor of Boston.

Mike Dukakis and I were aware of each other in the world of politics. We also rubbed elbows a bit socially. Back in those days, Mike and his wife Kitty spent a good bit of time during the summer on the Island of Nantucket. I think they had spent their honeymoon there. They had a few folks they were very close to and stayed with frequently. They were fans of Nantucket.

In those days I spent my summers in Nantucket. I must admit I was not a fan of Mike Dukakis. I found him aloof and remote in our occasional conversations. I suppose that somewhere in the back of my mind – and it was a politically ambitious mind – I sensed that Mike and I might be on a collision course with our ambitions. He was also an ambitious politician.

In fact, that collision did occur when the Boston mayor chose Dukakis instead of me to run for lieutenant governor with him when the Mayor ran for Governor. That collision was some years ahead of us, however, when, in the summer of 1969, I found myself at a cocktail party on Nantucket with State Representative Mike and wife Kitty in attendance.

As often happens to me at cocktail parties, I found myself in the kitchen. I was nursing a beer in a corner when Mike Dukakis came in and stood with me. I had a feeling he had been looking for me. We exchanged some brief chitchat and then, after a few moments of silence, Dukakis looked at me and said, "I want to tell you something I've been thinking about." He paused. I waited. "Something about you and me," he added, and then very firmly said, "One of us, you or me, is going to run for President of the United States."

Within a few years of that prediction, my political career was destroyed by my folly, and that, oh so fitting Greek word, hubris, and the deceitful machinations of the Boston mayor. I retreated to Nantucket to live and make a life.

In the summer of 1988, Michael Dukakis was nominated by the Democratic Party as their candidate for the presidency. In the excitement and, I can imagine, the euphoria of that evening, Dukakis was congratulated by one of his Nantucket friends. The fellow said Mike was unusually animated. "I hear Jack Warner is still living on Nantucket," Dukakis said. "When you get home, I want you to ask him if he remembers something I told him one summer night almost twenty years ago." He told the man of his prediction. When the fellow returned home, he sought me out.

"Did he really say that?" he gushed. "Do you remember that?"

"Yes," I said. "He really said it and I do remember."

# Come Right In, Senator

There was a strange fellow from the North Shore of Boston who served as a State Senator for many years. His name in this story will be William Small, but to all hands he was known as "Billy." He was just one of an assemblage of characters. Many men in the legislature have been known to have what might be called multiple personalities by some or leading double lives by others.

There were men from the other end of the state who lived with "other women" on Monday, Tuesday and Wednesday nights – with an occasional Thursday – for years. The legislature almost never sat on Fridays. The main problem for these representatives of the people was handling phone calls from the little woman at home. These were dealt with in various ingenious ways. One speaker of the house some years ago handled the problem by becoming a bigamist.

A lesser problem were the occasional demands – sometimes strident – by various pressure groups to restrict the number of days the legislature could sit. The Massachusetts Legislature meets on a practically January to Christmas schedule. It has the longest sessions of any legislature in America, maybe the world. Cutting the session would badly curtail the idyllic lives of those pols who came from far enough to stay overnight. It would also reduce the time and travel payments that all senators and reps quietly receive.

Any attempts to curtail the long hardworking days of the Massachusetts Legislature have been almost unanimously defeated on every occasion. For years the leader of the anti-shorten-the-session group was a legislator from Hampshire County in Western Mass. This was a very hard drinking former milkman who would begin his drinking on Monday morning when he arrived in Boston.

He would drink steadily until Thursday when he joined his colleagues for the return trip to the Golden West.

In his hometown he was Mister Sobriety. He was the reformed drinker. No matter what the occasion in his district, he would not use alcohol. His wife would beam at him at social events when he was offered a taste of demon rum and proudly – and loudly – announce, "Oh, no thank you, Charles doesn't take anything."

In his home district our man was a ruddy-faced teetotaler. There was a great deal of puzzlement among the locals when he died and the word was cirrhosis.

To get back to Senator Billy – he was another master of the double life but in quite a different way. His was a Jekyll and Hyde personality. Up in his district on the North Shore he was known as the kindest, most thoughtful, genial, caring man that the Good Lord had ever sent to do good for others. He was beloved for doing errands "down in Boston" for constituents. Errands that might consist of exchanging Mrs. Brown's dress that she bought in a sale at Filene's for credit, or picking up some merchandise at Jordan's that Mrs. Smith had ordered. That was "Good ol' Billy" – the lovely, thoughtful man who was their state senator.

When he got to Boston, Good ol' Billy became someone else. He was an overbearing, pompous, vain bully who made sure everyone called him Senator Small. His thoughtful errands were run by kids working at the State House who lived in fear of the lash of his tongue. I saw him turn long-suffering secretaries – professional women – into sobbing abject creatures with his intimidating, tormenting behavior. He took a not well hidden pleasure in using his power on people in his kingdom in Boston where he was a mean, nasty son of a bitch.

One day Good ol' Billy was in his home district and as usual he was doing good for others. In this case he was attending the funeral of a constituent and was honoring that poor soul by joining his comrades in the Knights of Columbus. They marched into the church in the flamboyant uniforms of Catholic nobility dressed as Spanish Grandees. No one more noble or grand than Good ol'

Billy, who, as Grand Knight, wore his sword and epaulets; his blue tricorner hat had the especially large white plume given to the leader.

After the Mass, as the Knights marched out in their splendor, a weeping woman approached the Senator.

"Oh, Billy, I need your help. The family needs your help. They've taken my Joe up to the Hill." (*The Hill* was what the grim, faded brick, monstrous building of the state mental hospital that loomed outside the town was called).

"What happened?" Good ol' Senator Billy asked.

"Oh, we had some trouble in the neighborhood last night and the cops came and I dunno – they ended up taking Joe up to the Hill. You gotta' get him out, Billy. He's not really crazy."

Good ol' Billy Small thought quickly – not one of his strong points, since by actual, undeniable count he had set a state record of having taken the bar exam twenty-one times without success. The Senator figured the time to get to the cemetery, for the Knights to assemble, the priests to arrive – they were always late – he could stop by the State Hospital, grab the Superintendent by the lapels and get Joe released. Maybe bring him to the cemetery rites with him in triumph.

"Don't worry," he said to the forlorn wife. "I'll get him out right away."

Good ol' Senator Billy Small, Grand Protector of the Knights of Columbus, got into his car, making sure that he held down the plume on his hat as he got behind the wheel, and off he rode to the mental hospital, his elegant head gear firmly in place. His sword buckled on to his sparkling white belt.

The guards at the hospital were two men he didn't know. They both stared at him with strange expressions as he got out of the car. He announced that he was Senator Small and wanted to be taken immediately to the superintendent. The imperious Billy of the State House took over as they continued to stare at him. His voice rose with strident demands and then threats to their jobs. The guards moved quickly, one to each side of him and held him firmly.

113

"Come right in, Senator. Everything will be just fine."

It was not until the next day that the Senator was released. Strangely, he was more arrogant than ever. He had a piece of paper that certified him mentally competent. He frequently waved that paper at his colleagues during debates in the Senate.

"I have just returned from Boston. It is the only sane thing to do if you find yourself there."

—*Letter from comedian Fred Allen, Boston native, to Groucho Marx*

# Our Friend the Policeman

I was always impressed with the senior officers I met in the Marine Corps. Yet, the truth is, I've never been a fan of authority. I'm not a big booster of the cops. The way things are going here in the USA, that could be a big problem for me if I were younger because I reckon the way the terrorism business is booming, we'll have a cop of some kind or other on every street corner.

An awful lot of cops seem very taken with the extraordinary power they have – they have good reason. I think it was Justice Holmes who said, "There is no individual power in this country equal to that of the cop on the beat," – or today, a cop in a cruiser.

I had a dear pal who spent a bit of time doing police work. He was not a fellow who enjoyed throwing his weight around, in truth his *modus vivendi*, even when he became a lawyer and a political force, was to keep a low profile. He was always very casual about his police work.

His first policing was done for the U. S. Army. My pal was an eighteen year old soldier in the bloody battle for Okinawa. When the battle was over, he was detailed to guard Japanese prisoners.

The prisoners were put to work digging trenches and laying drainage pipe. One baking hot morning, my friend was watching his charges work and getting more and more upset with them. The once savage enemies couldn't seem to make any sense out of the job they were doing. Finally in disgust, he told the terrified, stumbling interpreter to tell the men to get out of the trench. He would show them how to connect and lay the pipe. He put down his rifle and jumped into the trench and got to work.

A couple of dozen close-cropped, dark-skinned heads loomed over the hole and watched him intently. He played show-and-tell with the fascinated prisoners and then spotted his loaded M-1 rifle lying in the midst of them.

Slowly – breathing long, deep breaths – slowly, he climbed out of the trench and casually, thanking God as he did, picked up his rifle. The little Japs beamed and nodded and smiled and got back to work.

When he returned to civilian life, our friend the soldier became our friend the policeman. He attended college and law school and, while doing that, as policemen say, he went "on the job" as a Boston cop.

As a rookie he quickly learned how the seniority system worked. His first lesson was dramatic, nasty, and very public. He and his senior partner were working the Copley Square area. The superintendent of an apartment building reported a "terrible odor" coming from one of his apartments and said the fellow who lived there had not been seen for some time.

The two policemen and the super tried every possible key and wedge to open the apartment door from which a "terrible odor" was certainly seeping. They gave up and quickly and gratefully went outside.

Two uniformed cops and a third man assembled on a sidewalk in Copley Square. Pointing at a certain second floor window can draw a crowd – and they did. The number of onlookers grew larger and larger after the senior cop ordered a ladder to be produced by the super. While the senior man watched, our friend and the superintendent positioned the ladder so that it was propped just beneath the ledge of the window of the odiferous apartment.

Our friend looked at the super who vigorously shook his head. Then he looked at his senior who pointed a finger at him and then up at the window. Slowly our friend climbed the ladder. He could feel the eyes of the crowd on him. The smell was an awful, toxic enveloping force pushing against him as he got up to the window. When his hands reached the bottom of the window, he tried in vain to push upwards. He pulled his gun out of his holster and heard the crowd murmur below him. He held the pistol by the barrel and moved another rung up and looked in the window. What he saw he could never forget or erase from his mind's eye.

It was as bad as anything he had seen on Okinawa. The man was sitting upright, he had to be in a chair, but the body was so swollen that the chair could not be seen. He wore eyeglasses, grotesquely sunk into the skin of the face. Numbing all the horror of the scene, however, was the smell – not to be described or imagined.

Our friend balanced himself, covered his mouth and nose with his handkerchief, and broke the glass in the window. The gust of foulness that hit him almost knocked him off the ladder.

He managed to unlock the window. He tumbled into the room. He tried to ignore the body but was further appalled to note the swelling had burst the man's clothes. He raced across the room and fumbled wildly with the three locks on the door, managed to kick up the angle-bar restrainer, open the door, and sprint into the hallway. He was throwing up when the door slammed shut behind him. He leaned against the wall and closed his eyes for a long moment.

He cleaned himself up as he went slowly down the stairs, onto the street, and without saying a word in response to the puzzled look of his partner, he began to slowly climb the ladder again.

Years of night school classes rolled on, and our friend the policeman found, to his delight, that he now had a junior partner.

Our friend had formed a rigid rule as he observed his fellow policemen through the years.

The rule was very simple: Do not get involved.

He learned early that the senior man decided whether he wanted to be the driver or the passenger in the cruiser. Our friend was the driver – always. He felt it was his job to protect the vehicle. In virtually every emergency he did his duty as he saw it and stayed at his post behind the wheel of the valuable car that the city provided for the safety of the citizenry.

One summer day after a Red Sox game, our friend and his partner were called to an accident scene in the Fenway. Traffic was snarled up for blocks. When they arrived, the junior man debarked and quickly returned to advise our friend to call emergency for an ambulance. Soon two more cruisers arrived. A large crowd gathered. An ambulance screamed along sidewalks and nosed through the crowd.

Our friend did not desert his post behind the wheel where he discretely read the *Record American* laid out on the seat beside him.

Later, as the ambulance wailed away, our friend's partner returned to the cruiser and sank wearily into his seat. He took off his cap and wiped his forehead. "By God," he said, "that wasn't pretty."

"Geez," said our friend, "where was O'Malley? He could get in a jam over this. He's supposed to be working that corner."

His junior partner turned and gave our friend a long stare. "Who the hell do you think we just put in that ambulance?"

There are, of course, exceptions to every rule. There was an occasion that our friend the policeman had to be a bit less inflexible with his rigid avoidance of the world outside his cruiser.

In truth, it wasn't really his fault. He was blindsided by celebrity. Every American knows from an early age that there are different rules for celebrities. Policemen especially know this.

The celebrity in question was named Arthur Fiedler. He was the white-maned impresario of the Boston Symphony and the Boston Pops. He was a real live Boston icon. In those days, he would top most lists as Boston's Number 1 Celebrity. He was also a fanatic about attending fires; night or day, sunshine, rain or snow, the great conductor got to the fires. He had been appointed an honorary fire chief. A fire chief's helmet had been bestowed on his leonine head. With or without his bedazzling cover, when the bells rang – he had one alarm system in his house and one in his office – honorary Chief Fiedler was there.

Late one evening, our friend was stationed in his cruiser on Beacon Hill while his partner worked at controlling the crowd that was gawking at a rather sizeable fire in a townhouse. As his gaze shifted from the fire to the crowd to the book lying on the seat beside him, he noticed a paddy wagon pull up and back in beside one of the fire engines.

A few minutes later his partner came to the car. He was disheveled and his face reflected the anger that his voice contained.

"God damn, there's a lot of nuts in this town." He reached in and grabbed his charge book.

"What happened?" our friend asked.

"Some God damned nutcake running around playing fireman – in a tuxedo for Christ sake. I'm gonna charge him. The foolish bastard's a menace. I told him twice to get out of there – I tossed him in the wagon."

Our friend grunted.

"Some of the fire guys knew him, I think. He must drive them nuts – a fire bug – probably started the fire – think's he's a big shot." He paused in his writing. "Ever hear of a guy named – let's see – F I E D L E R?"

Our friend the policeman was up out of his seat in the cruiser as though catapulted. "You get in the car." he said to his partner. "I'll handle this."

And handle it, he did. Maestro-Fire Chief Fiedler was personally escorted back into the fire scene.

Our friend left the police department soon after that, began a law practice and ran for public office.

Mr. Arthur Fiedler, the great conductor, was one of his early contributors.

# The Power of Television

I have a good pal in Boston. When I lived there we spent a lot of time together. He was in politics and was as shrewd an observer of the local and national scene as anyone I've ever known. My friend, we'll call him Harry, was also a lawyer, so with his position as an elected official, his law practice, and a married man with a large family, he was a very busy fellow.

In the course of being busy, he made the acquaintance of a young lady whose company he enjoyed. This caused him to be even busier. So busy that he began arriving home later and later at night. Or, if you prefer, earlier and earlier in the morning.

Unbeknownst to me, I was being fingered as the culprit who was causing my pal to spend these long hours away from home.

It was well known to his wife – and other wives – that I loved to sit and talk and drink beer with my friends. So it was that Harry used me as his excuse when his wife – we'll call her Helen – began to question him about his exhaustive schedule. "You know how Jack is," Harry would say. "He wants to sit and talk all night. It's awful – he's such a night bird. But he's my friend and he's got some personal problems right now so I just can't ignore him. So I drink my beer and listen and try to be helpful."

This routine went on for quite a while. I was in Helen's company a couple of times during this period. We had always gotten along very well – with lots of chuckles. Things seemed different – I thought I might have offended her with some flip remark because there were no chuckles. She seemed cool to me. I mentioned my concern to Harry but he assured me I still had a fan in Helen.

In those days, the Boston Celtics were the toast of the town and of New England. That year – to the delight of sports fans up and down the East Coast – the Celtics ended up in the championship finals against the New York Knicks.

I had some good friends who played on that Celtics team, so I was a committed fan. One of the players gave me a couple of tickets for what looked to be the decisive game at Madison Square Garden in New York. I flew down to New York with another friend – it did not happen to be Harry.

I got to the Garden early to watch the pre-game warm-up. While hanging around courtside, one of the announcers for the game, who I happened to know, asked me if I'd like to be on television at half-time to discuss the game. Hey! Would I like to be on national television at half time to discuss the fine points of this crucial Celtics-Knicks game?

I guess I would.

I did and I reveled in it.

I imagined the faces of friends and loved ones across the country when they saw the new basketball expert on their TV screens.

That night, or rather, early the next morning, Harry tiptoed into his kitchen and found Helen sitting at the kitchen table. "Well," she said, "what's tonight's story?"

"What do you mean 'story?'" an offended and weary Harry replied.

"Who were you with?"

"Who was I with? I was with that Goddamn Jack. He just keeps on going. Boy can that guy talk and drink beer! He's wearing me out."

"What about the Celtics game?"

"What about it?"

"Well, as you say, he's a nut on the Celtics – didn't you watch the game? You must have – the kids and I watched it."

"Oh, sure, we were at Nick's in the North End and we had the game on. Sure."

"You and Jack at Nick's in the North End and you watched the game?"

"That's right."

We can only imagine what Helen's face must have looked like during this conversation.

"You've always said that Jack is an unusual guy, Harry. And now I know you're right."

"What do you mean?"

"Jack was interviewed on television during the half-time of the Celtics game. He was there in New York, sitting with the announcers at the game. We watched him. Your children and your wife, we watched him on television. He is a remarkable guy to get back and forth to Nicks in the North End like that – you lying son-of-a-bitch."

I will not burden you with further details of that conversation. I am happy to report that Harry and Helen are still married, and in fact are preparing for a big celebration of their fiftieth.

It just goes to show the power of television.

# A Memory of
# Ray Fitzgerald

I had the privilege of being a friend of Ray Fitzgerald. We grew up in Westfield, Massachusetts. He was older than I. A legendary high school athlete in baseball and basketball. He was my hero. I thought he represented what every young man should aspire to. I still do. He was gifted in so many ways, yet humble, witty, and caring. Ray Fitzgerald was as fine a human being as I have ever known.

Years later, Ray and I were part owners of the weekly newspaper in Westfield, before he left for fame – and no fortune – as one of America's finest sports writers with the *Boston Globe*. Journalism schools would do well to seek out copies of the *Westfield News Advertiser* of the mid-1960's. Fitz wrote almost all of the paper and it was marvelous to read.

I have many memories of Ray. One in particular is a stunning example of the power of his gentle nature that Dan Shaughnessy refered to in his August 24, 1999 *Boston Globe* column.

Ray and I and another friend went to a Giant's–Cleveland Browns game at Yankee Stadium. After the game, we moved with the crowd across the street from the stadium. As we moseyed along the sidewalk, suddenly, two steps in front of us four or five young men walking with the crowd began to argue, voices suddenly shrill. In an instant – a moment that changed our post-game euphoria to tense, alert, shocked watchfulness – one of the group, all of them youths, plunged his hand in his pocket and whipped out a slim object that, with a snap, became a long, thin-bladed stiletto. You could hear and feel the onlookers catch their breath. The boy with the knife began to stalk another boy who slowly circled around him, his eyes wide and fixed on the knife.

No one else moved except Ray Fitzgerald. He walked between the knife and its intended. He kept his eyes on the fellow with the knife. His voice was low, calm, almost chatty. "Don't do something that you'll regret for the rest of your life. Think for a moment what using that knife could mean to the both of you." He held out his hand and said, "That knife won't make your life better." He was speaking very gently. No one in the crowd of onlookers or the participants moved or spoke. "Give me the knife," Ray said quietly, extending his hand. "The knife won't help you." He slowly took the knife from the boy's hand and without another word walked over to a nearby trash barrel and tossed it in. The crowd stared in silent wonder. They had seen a remarkable act by a remarkable man.

# Jesse and Der Fuhrer

One of the best guys I've ever known is Tom "Satch" Sanders. He played for the Boston Celtics for thirteen years. He was a key ingredient in that famous team's mix that caused them to win eight championships while he played. He later coached the Celtics and coached at Harvard. He is now a Deputy Commissioner of the National Basketball Association. Through the years, Tom and I have been through a number of intense personal events together. He is one of my dearest friends. Through Satch, I made another good friend. His name was Jesse Owens.

If you are of a certain age, that statement will have meaning. For the rest of you, let me tell you about him – and why being with him put me in a position to listen to the most predictable person-to-person responses I've ever known.

Jesse was a black man born in Alabama in 1913, raised in Cleveland, Ohio where his parents went looking for something better than the poor dirt of Alabama.

In high school, Jesse revealed an extraordinary talent for running and jumping. He tied the world record for the 100-yard dash and came within inches of breaking the world record for the broad jump. Jesse chose to go to Ohio State to college. There were no scholarships for black athletes in 1933. He studied, worked part-time jobs, and ran for the track team – and, oh, how he ran. At a Big Ten track meet in Ann Arbor Michigan in 1935, in the span of forty-five minutes, he set three world records and tied a fourth; in the 220 yard dash, the broad jump, and the 220 low hurdles he set world marks and tied the record for the 100-yard dash.

So it was a given that Jesse would be a representative of the United States in the upcoming Olympic Games.

126

The 1936 Olympic Games were to be held in Berlin. The timing and the place to choose the world's finest athletes created a fascinating historical moment. One that would stay in the memory of much of the western world, despite, or because of, the savage events that were about to engulf them.

The Berlin Olympics were more than Germany's Olympics. They belonged to the man to whom Germany belonged, Adolph Hitler.

For Hitler the circumstances could not have been better. He had the perfect setting to display to the world the awesome combination of muscle, metal and mysticism his dictatorship had perfected. In the theatrical setting of the Olympic Stadium, where the drama of the Nazi movement could be displayed, Der Fuhrer could prove to the world his proclamations that the Germans were truly a master race.

To young Americans about to test their athletic skills against the rest of the world, Hitler's histrionics were only of passing notice, but millions of people watched him with fascination tinged with fear. The Olympics provided a stage for Hitler to strut and for the world to observe and wonder.

Ironically, the person who came to dominate the stage was a twenty-three year old black American: Jesse Owens set four world records – won four gold medals – in one afternoon. He ran Hitler's theory of the master race right out of the stadium.

That in itself would seem to be the story of a lifetime, but those triumphs would be overshadowed by what happened next. It was Hitler's order that the Gold Medal winners be brought to his private box which was set front and center in the stadium so that all eyes could feast on the Fuhrer.

One by one the gold medal winners were escorted to Adolph Hitler's box which was crowded with the be-medaled Reichmarshal Goering and the elite of the Nazi state. Photos show each one outdoing the other in smiling sycophancy at their leader as he bestowed congratulations on the winners and shook their hands.

Photos also show the incident that Americans of certain age

never forgot. I can swear to that. Jesse Owens, hero of the Olympics, was escorted to Hitler's box. Der Furher stared at the slim handsome black man for a moment while the great track star tentatively offered his hand. Hitler slowly and deliberately turned his back on Jesse, ignoring the outstretched hand.

I met Jesse in Boston in the mid 60's. Through some kind of chemistry, we became good friends; we had many meals together. Jesse loved lobster. We both liked to drink beer and tell stories. We did a lot of that for a number of years. Whenever his travels brought him to town he would call. He was always amiable and sweet tempered. A gentleman in every circumstance.

When I was a young fellow, I used to hear people say, as a fact of life, that all Chinese looked alike and the Chinese couldn't tell one white ghost from another, and white folks couldn't tell one Negro from another. I'm here to tell you that wasn't true about white people and Jesse Owens; he seemed to be instantly recognized by people of a certain age. The scenario never varied. People would approach hesitantly, they might hover nearby and whisper among themselves. When they spoke it was always with deference. Jesse always received them politely. He was the most courteous of men.

The pattern of the questions was uncanny – it never varied and it went like this:

"Excuse me?" The questioners were always white.

"Yes?" If we were sitting, Jesse would get to his feet. He was always immaculately dressed: sport coat and tie, well-pressed slacks; he always looked very fit; hardly a grey hair.

"Are you..." (pause, a little uneasy, then a rush of words) "Are you Jesse Owens?"

"Yes, I am."

"My God – I told you so, Helen," or Harry or whoever.

"Gosh, I'd like to shake your hand, my name is _____."

Jesse would shake hands with the person or group, and then it came: a gambler could have won huge sums on this next question. It always was asked – never failed.

"Do you mind if I ask, well – how old are you?"

The questioner might act uneasy or abashed, but they had to ask – they had to. I came to understand the scene in their minds was of Alolph Hitler and Jesse.

Hitler, who dominated the world in the 30's and 40's – the architect of World War II which was now history. Hitler and his savage associates standing, staring at Jesse and turning away. A scene from the history books from a world long gone. They had seen the pictures. The most famous social snub the people of a certain age had ever known. Many may have sensed the picture was of repressed violence – certain to explode one day. The explosion would rip the world apart. The major players all dead with the exception of this slim handsome black gentleman who at that moment had been at the center of it all. He was from a lost dreadful world – an almost mythic place. Now he was standing, polite, gentle and genial. Every time, you could tell, it was creating a special memory for people when they shook Jesse's hand.

One night after one of these moments – and they happened very often – Jesse smiled at me over his beer and said, "You know, life is funny, Jack. Set four world records in the Olympics, and what people remember is that Hitler wouldn't shake hands with me. Hell, he sure wasn't the first person who had refused to take my hand."

# The Kids Would
# Go In There

I sat down today and wrote this title at the top of the page. It's a story about my friend Wayne Embry and myself, and the City of Boston. It's an all too accurate story of how sometimes government doesn't function.

Wayne Embry had played professional basketball for many years. He is a very smart guy. He's also probably the biggest man I've ever known in my life. And I'll add, one of the best.

Wayne played for the Cincinnati Royals for years and the team never won a championship. It was his goal to play on a team that would be the world champions of professional basketball. So Wayne retired from the Cincinnati team figuring that after his retirement the phone would ring with the right person on the other end. He was right. When the phone rang, it was Red Auerbach of the Boston Celtics calling. Wayne came out of retirement and played on two World Champion Celtics teams. Then he retired for real.

I was Commissioner of Parks and Recreation for the City of Boston. I thought it would be a great idea to make Wayne Director of Recreation for the City of Boston. Here was a black man with impeccable credentials who would focus his charm and hard work on the kids of the city. I hired Wayne. Some people thought it was a great idea; others didn't, including the mayor. It was the beginning of a bad split between the mayor and myself.

To go with Wayne as Director of Recreation, I started a summer basketball program that still exists. We put lights in six or eight playgrounds and started summer night basketball, which we called Boston Neighborhood Basketball Association — BNBA.

One day, Wayne and I were touring the various city-owned

gyms in the city, which were now being kept open during daylight hours so the kids could practice to get ready for their league games. When we arrived at a gym in the South End, it was around eleven o'clock in the morning. There were a dozen or so kids sitting on the steps of the gym. Of course, they all made a big fuss about Wayne, asking for autographs and shaking that big hand. I went up and tried the door of the gym and found it locked. I asked one of the kids why the gym was locked. He shrugged and told me it was usually locked. I asked him if he knew where the workers were. He pointed at the tavern across the street.

Wayne and I walked across the street to the tavern. Our entrance caused absolute silence to prevail. I spotted one of the keepers of the gym and asked him to come outside. He put his beer down and walked out with me. I looked across the street and said to him, "You know, the door is locked over there?"

"Sure, Commissioner," he said brightly.

"Why is that?" I asked.

"Well," he said. "If we didn't keep it locked, the kids would go in there."

I suppose some of you are wondering about the number of coincidences that occur in these stories. Well, here's another one. As I was writing this this morning, the phone rang. It was Wayne Embry. I hadn't talked with him for over a year. After Wayne left Boston, he became coach of the Milwaukee Bucks and then of the Cleveland Cavaliers. He then became President and General Manager of the Cleveland Cavaliers, and in that position was nice enough to vote for me to become Commissioner of the National Basketball Association. Wayne was calling to tell me that he was writing a book and he wanted to go over the details of the story of the guy who kept the gym locked because "the kids would go in there."

I wished Wayne great success with his book.

# A Bad Habit

If old hotels could talk they would have the most arresting stories. Writers have known that since Chaucer. The Old Vendome Hotel at the corner of Commonwealth and Dartmouth Streets in Boston could have furnished a riviting television series. The awful deaths of nine firefighters trapped in the crashing cauldron of one section of the building in the 70's would furnish a crushing, wrenching last chapter. There had been over one hundred years of drama in the Vendome before the final fiery ending.

A fellow named Sid Kleve was manager and part owner of the hotel when I knew it. He was a thin, droopy looking guy with a sad face that I figured came from listening to so many sad stories from his guests, most of whom seemed as worn down as the hotel. The hours Sid spent at his hotel would have made Clark Kent thin and droopy.

Before I moved my family to Boston I shared a room in the hotel with a sports writer pal of mine who was on his way to conquering the Boston and New England newspaper world. We got to know many of the players involved in the Vendome's dramatics. The hotel was home to many of the guests.

Of course, life's eternal stage is a pub. The Vendome had two – one off the lobby which was known as the upstairs bar and another in the basement. Upstairs was an intimate room with a C-shaped bar set against the wall. The space was done in a dark green with green and blue velvet wall covering. There was room for four or five chairs at the bar and three or four small tables. Twenty patrons were a jam in the place. With the old wood and the wall cover it was like having a drink in the 19th century.

In fact, velvet wall coverings were selectively viewable in another place in the hotel. If you were a favorite of Sid Kleve's –

and I was – there was a suite on the second floor corner of the hotel that was done in velvet and damask. The bedroom and sitting room looked out on Commonwealth Avenue. The suite had been decorated for – believe it or not – Sarah Bernhardt, a world famous actress of the turn of the century. Sid kept fresh flowers in the faded room and would show it with great pride. He changed nothing there except the flowers. I think it was his little island of peace in the sometimes frantic goings on in the hotel.

The center of much of the hotel's personality was the chief bartender, Justin Quinn. Justin was a tall, black curly haired, blue-eyed Irishman whose strong jaw could not quite camouflage the weakness his puffy skin and rheumy eyes betrayed. Those flaws were soon forgotten when Justin started talking. He could, and would, talk on any subject – and he often knew what he was talking about. His claim to fame was that he had been appointed to the curious position of City Greeter in the no-nonsense administration of Mayor John Collins. No doubt about it, Justin, especially in the bar, was a hell of a greeter.

He opened the upstairs bar at about three in the afternoon. The Boston advertising crowd would start filtering in about then. They were a heady, funny mix, generally smart and hip. Justin held court behind his little bar in the cozy room like a prime minister.

When I first met Justin I noticed that he would occasionally sip from what I thought was a glass of coke as he presided over his little kingdom. In time I learned that the drink was a very dark Manhattan. Some sippin'.

Justin would close the upstairs bar around 7:30 – by then the hip crowd would have been charmed and gone. Then he would go downstairs to the bistro bar in the basement – a lounge with a good-sized bar, a small dance floor and Glenn Miller and Sinatra music on a jukebox. The bistro bar was done in pink with low lights and I guess you could say a certain number of low lifes. It was a place for seekers and cheaters and guys and gals hanging around in hope as they looked at the young lovers.

Justin would have one or two assistants in the bistro. He was supposed to be the boss, but he would run out of gas by nine o'clock. He would sometimes fold his arms on the bar and put his head down. Sid would come down and wake him gently and lead him upstairs. Sid was like a despairing father with Justin but he never got angry with him, only shook his head sorrowfully.

Certainly Justin was the reason that the upstairs cozy was jammed five days a week and moved a lot of booze. The advertising crowd were not beer drinkers and Justin also attracted players to the downstairs joint who stayed late. But it was more than the business for Sid. He kept a kind eye on all his help. There was an old lady who ran an older switchboard in the lobby. Everyone knew she listened to everybody's phone conversations – and repeated them to other regulars. Sid would listen to complaints but there was no way he would move her.

Maybe it was not so strange that a death dealing fire would spell the end of the Vendome because the place seemed to have much more than its share of fires. One of them featured the switchboard lady in the center of things.

The hotel fire alarms woke us one night at about 3:00 a.m. A very colorful group congregated in the lobby. I remember one old Englishman who lived in the hotel and was a regular of Justin's was wearing highly polished boots, jodhpurs, a bright red hunting jacket and a bowler hat. He told me they were his most sacred possessions. "If they burn, I burn," he said emphatically.

The crowd eyed one another with no attempt to disguise curiosity. There were some very interesting outfits and people. There were occasional peeks at rather flamboyant nightwear. The lobby was getting smokey – some folks were standing outside in the very cold. Grumbling increased – where the hell was the fire department? I went over to the switchboard lady, part of the group tagging behind me.

"How long ago did you call the fire department?" I asked.

"I didn't," she said primly, not looking at me.

"You didn't call in this fire?"

"No."

"Why?"

"Mr. Kleve told me not to be calling the fire department all the time. He said we're having too many fires. It's giving the hotel a bad reputation. So, I'm not calling them."

There was swearing and shouting in exasperated can-you-believe-it tones behind me.

"Call them right now," I said.

She looked at me through old glasses.

"Call now," I repeated.

"Well, I'm going to tell Mr. Kleve that you insisted."

The fire department put the fire out quickly but there was another fire smouldering in the Vendome.

Justin was thinking about leaving.

It all began just about the time I moved my family to Boston. Justin announced he'd been asked to apply for the job of Director of Public Relations for a large, prestigious Catholic girl's school just outside of Boston, a school known to one and all.

The job became a major topic of discussion in the upstairs bar. Justin wanted everyone's opinion. Should he or shouldn't he? Would the school accept a working bartender?

My visits were infrequent now but the Justin's job theme continued. Justin was urged by one and all to apply. All except Sid Kleve who took me aside one day to tell me mournfully, "I don't think it's a good idea."

Finally, Justin announced he was going to apply. He would accept the challenge to change his life. His wife was going to daily Mass praying for his triumph. Several of us were asked to write letters of recommendation to the Reverend Mother, President of the College. After much discussion the application was submitted with our letters. A few weeks later Justin was interviewed. He shared the questions and answers. They were debated in the bar. Now a large number of regulars crossed shaky fingers and wished Justin success.

Then – *marveloso!* – Justin got the job. The old City Greeter would be back in the limelight. His name would be in the papers again. There had to be a celebration – and there was. The advertising gang put on a dinner in the old hotel dining room that Sid opened for the night. A sweet affair, a big crowd, Justin's wife and kids were there. He was given an envelope of cash and a gift certificate for a new suit at Brooks Brothers.

Sid Kleve sat beside me at the head table. He offered a benevolent smile to the crowd and made a nice little speech about Justin and his family, but three or four times during the meal he turned to me and quietly groaned, "I don't like it, I just don't like it."

In those days I frequently walked to work in the morning. My route took me through the Public Garden. It was May and a walk through the Boston Public Garden must be as fine a way to start the day as America has to offer. One morning who did I spot sitting on a bench near the great equestrian statue of George Washington but Justin Quinn. He was reading a newspaper. I gave him a "Hi, how ya doin?" He returned a smile and offered a warm "Never better, never better."

A couple days later there was Justin again. The newspaper was folded. He got up when he saw me.

"Jack, I need to talk to you – can you give me a minute?"

He looked sharp in his Brooks Brothers suit.

"Sure, why don't we sit here?"

We sat. I turned to him, "What's going on?"

"It's about the job," he said and suddenly there in the morning sunshine he began to weep. "I've been standing over by the Ritz watching you walk through here for days trying to get up the nerve to talk to you."

"You lost your job."

"No." He was crying hard now. "There never was a job."

I had to catch my breath. I repeated his words as a question. "There never was a job?"

"I got started with the story and it just kept growing. I couldn't stop. I had to keep going. I couldn't stop. Now I get up every morning and come in town – hang around, go to the library. I can't let my wife know, my kids. There isn't any job. There never was any job. Jack, will you help me?" He was shaking with anguish.

"What do you want me to do?"

"Will you go see Sid? Talk to him. See if he'll take me back."

I went to see Sid Kleve.

He didn't seem too surprised.

He took Justin back.

# Chapter 2

Years later the Vendome had suffered its final tragic fire. It was now a building of expensive condominiums. The world had changed.

I was with two friends of mine in Stockbridge, Massachusetts – way out in Berkshire County. I always thought it wasn't an accident that Norman Rockwell lived in Stockbridge. The quintessential artist of America in the most American of towns.

The three of us were having lunch in the Pub at the Red Lion, which is the perfect inn for the perfect town. There was Frank Sargent, Lieutenant Governor of Massachusetts and soon to be Governor, Don Dwight, soon to be Lieutenant Governor and myself. I was a State Public Works Commissioner and I envisioned a north-south highway for the Berkshires. I wanted these two as allies. I had already got the highway idea in circulation with a public hearing.

The three of us were good friends and our lunch was relaxed with lots of laughter. A fellow sitting with a group at another table got up and headed toward our table. I noticed him as he came and decided he was an unhappy fellow. He marched right up to the table and planted himself.

"You guys have one hell of a nerve coming in here and laughin' it up after what you did."

The laughter stopped and the three of us stared at him. He pointed a finger at Frank Sargent.

137

"You're Sargent, right? Lieutenant Governor – gonna be Governor next week when Volpe bails out to Washington. Well, you're a nervy bastard."

This man was pointing his finger at the single most confrontational avoiding man in the world – at least the world I knew. I almost laughed looking at Frank. As I told him later, I was sure he was debating denying who he was.

The finger swung to me. "Warner! Ha, you want to build a north-south highway. That will be some project! Probably never start – or if it does, never finish, the way you keep appointments."

"Mister," I said, "obviously you've got a problem with us. What is it?"

"You know Goddamn well what it is."

"No," I said, "I don't. Do you guys?"

They both uttered emphatic "no's" as they gave the fellow frowned-forehead stares.

"You don't know anything about the Southern Berkshire County Boosters dinner?" he asked sarcastically.

"No," I answered.

"The dinner you two were supposed to speak at," he barked. "You don't know that over three hundred tickets were sold to people who could ask you about the highway plan and ask the Governor about it too?" He had jolted even me into silence. "You don't know you were the guests of honor? And we all know you didn't show or bother to call. What a Goddamn insult."

"Wait a minute," I said.

"We waited too many minutes last Friday night."

"We know nothing about this, believe me," I said.

"What the hell is this all about?" Frank Sargent snapped.

"Yeah? Do you know a guy named Justin Quinn?" I nodded and started to speak, but he rolled right over me. "A friend of yours, right? You knew him in Boston, right? He runs the bar over at the Log Cabin. He set it up for you guys to come out here."

Dwight knew Justin's story and groaned.

138

Finally I interrupted. "Goddamn," I said, "he's done it again!

"Sit down, please, mister. Let me explain this to you and I'll begin by telling you I haven't heard from or seen Justin for at least four years."

"Me either," said the Governor quickly.

"All right," I said, "let me tell you about a bad habit that Justin has."

# Hero Worship

As I said earlier, Ray Fitzgerald was the premiere sports writer in New England for many years during the 60's and 70's. He won every award available for his work which I'm sure would have included a Pulitzer if not for his tragic early death. He was the heart and soul of the *Boston Globe* sports section. I say heart and soul because this kindly, thoughtful, humble, witty character brightened the day of everyone with whom he came in contact in person or in print.

Ray and I grew up in the same hometown. He was a few years older and a marvelous baseball and basketball player. He was my hero. He is still my hero. I was honored to be part owner of a weekly newspaper with him.

Ray went to Notre Dame where he played baseball and basketball. His hero was a former Notre Dame man who had become a very famous sports writer. His name was Red Smith and he starred for the *New York Herald Tribune* and the *New York Times*. Ray revered Red Smith's work and, in the opinion of many, his work was at the same level.

On a fine fall afternoon, Ray was covering a Yale-Harvard game at the Yale Bowl. To his delight, just before the National Anthem, Red Smith, himself, in all his easy going, unstudied nonchalance, came into the press box and moved into the only seat still available. It was next to Ray Fitzgerald.

I've only read about Smith, but I was a close pal of Ray's, so I know I'm at least fifty percent accurate when I say that sitting there side-by-side were two of the most modest stars you'll ever meet.

As I recall, Ray told me that the afternoon went like this:

Smith sits down, opens a case which contains a small typewriter and a much battered flask.

Smith uncaps flask, takes a sip.

Ray Fitzgerald nervously introduces himself. "Hi, Red, I'm Ray Fitzgerald from the *Boston Globe*."

Glance and quick handshake from his hero.

"Nice to meet you, Fitz."

The football game begins.

Ray takes pages of notes, plots ball movement on field, meanwhile checking his hero out of the corner of his eye.

Red sips from his flask – once or twice, and maybe three times in the course of the entire game scribbles a note on a small pad.

Game ends.

Ray, always a slow perfectionist, types and re-types his story.

The press box is now empty except for himself and his hero who has yet to write a word.

Ray is flabbergasted. Here is the outstanding sports writer in the United States – in the world – books have been written about him, books of his columns have been best sellers. Red Smith, Notre Dame's hero and his, sits sipping from his flask, staring out at the shadows filling the now cavernous old Yale Bowl.

Ray is just about finished, but he lingers. He cannot bring himself to leave yet. How does the Red Smith magic work? When does it work?

Slowly, Red rolls a piece of paper into his typewriter. He pauses, cocks his head, turns and says,

"Hey, Fitz, Orville was one of the Wright brothers, what was the other one's name?"

Red got the right answer from Ray, put his head down, and began to type without a pause. He was still banging away when Ray left the press box.

Ray Fitzgerald cut out Red Smith's column the next day, written about the Yale-Harvard game. He saved it. It was a classic and somehow or other, he led off with a reference to Wilbur and Orville Wright and their flying machine.

141

# Life is trouble.
## —Zorba the Greek

"There are only twenty thousand people in the world. All the rest is light and shadow."

*J. D. Warner*

In the great crap shoot called Life, one of the longest shots of all is adoption. I believe adoption is one of the most long-lasting, sensitive human undertakings. An awkward mix of nobility and selfishness. The wish for a family where there may be none, to expand or reinforce a marriage where there is fragility or disappointment, for kindness and care where there may be indifference. To fulfill and enrich lives that seem empty.

The reasons are many, but they are all intensely visceral. The goal is like the quest for the flash of green of a perfect sunset. The operative word is "hope" but in fact, adoption is fraught with peril on all sides.

This lottery-like grafting to form a family tree is after all a unique undertaking. It is a gamble and gamblers's stories are often fascinating. Here are a couple that might make you believe my theory that there are only 20,000 people in the world – all the rest is light and shadow.

# Semper Fi

A beautiful young woman, just graduated from high school, finds herself pregnant. Her young boyfriend, the first love of her life, makes himself scarce. She moves from her small town to the city and has her baby. Her sister helps her through her pain and assists in placing the baby boy for adoption.

The young lady goes to work by day and college by night. She is a very bright, witty woman. She receives her B.A. and continues on for a masters degree. One day on the campus she meets a handsome Marine Corps officer who is on a college recruiting visit. They fall in love. He asks her to marry him. She tells him the story of having the baby. He respects her and her story. They marry and have three children.

The Marine becomes a general. One day his wife tells him she must find the son she gave away. He agrees with her undertaking the search on two conditions: One, their children are not to be told – ever. Two, if she finds her son, she must not reveal herself to him – ever.

She begins the search and things fall in place rather easily. She acquires a copy of his college yearbook. His after-college goal – to become an officer in the United States Marines.

She shows this to her husband and asks for advice. He says he will think about it. The next evening they are having their pre-dinner drink and her husband says, "Your son is a captain in the Corps. He has a fine record. He will do well. He is presently on college recruiting duty." He pauses and looks into her tear-filled eyes. "You remember our agreement." She nods.

It takes her a day to find where her son is located. The day after a restless night she calls her Marine son. She identifies herself as the mother of a young man interested in "The Corps, as I understand you people call it." She explains that she must be anonymous because she does not want her son to think she is interfering with his life.

She and the captain have a marvelous conversation, a mix of serious and humorous. At one point, he says he would very much like to meet her son because "If he is like his mother, he must be a hell of a guy."

The mother stores that conversation, the sound of her son's voice, his laugh, his clear sincerity and commitment and self confidence in the treasury of her memory. She shares it with no one but brings it to the forefront of her mind and polishes its precious quality often.

She will probably never speak to her son again or ever see him. Yet she is well aware that "The Corps" is a small outfit and the general is some years from retirement.

# Addressee Unknown

A young woman – a girl of seventeen – defies her parents and decides to marry the boy down the street. He is nineteen. He defies his wealthy parents and they elope. A year later she realizes her parents were right. He is a liar and a faker, leading at least a double life. He has told the world he's in college. He is home sick for a few days so she uses a lunch hour from her job to go to the school and see if she can be helpful and bring home some books. She learns he is not enrolled in the college.

He admits the deception and says that actually he has a job and didn't want people to know he'd quit on college. A couple of weeks later, she calls him at work. The work place has never heard of him. She leaves her work early in tears and on the way home, walking past a local pub she spots him at a table with a woman who lives in their building.

She is eighteen years old with a zero for a husband, but that's not her biggest problem. She is pregnant – and she is being overwhelmed with advice, instructions, orders, demands that she should not keep the baby. This barrage comes from all directions. Her parents, her sister, his parents, and soon to be her ex-husband, who ironically happens to be an adopted child. Remember, this is forty years ago. Abortion is not a word that is used. Adoption is the option.

In the hospital after delivering a healthy little girl, the new mother finds her mother and sister by her bed. Her mother hands her a document which she can barely see through her tears. Her sister hands her a pen. The new mother asks to see and hold her baby one last time. She does and then signs the paper.

This happened many years ago on the East Coast of the United States.

The once young mother, now living on the West Coast and married to a fine steady man with whom she has a son and daughter decides to share the long hidden ache and loss within her. Her noble husband is understanding and supportive. She wants to find the little baby that was taken out of her arms. Her husband says he'll help her in any way he can. They decide not to tell their children any of this.

Her search is as intense as her emotions. She calls her lifelong friend in the East and asks her to go to the county record office and find the adoption name of the baby and the names of the adoptive parents.

Her friend spends days looking through twenty-four year-old records and finds the information. The baby has been given one of the three names the young mother had reviewed over and over in her "if it's a girl" daydreams during pregnancy.

The mother flies to the East Coast. She goes to the town where the child began growing up. The family moved once. Then twice more within the state. She goes to those towns. Finally, she gets the high school yearbook of her daughter, a beautiful girl, as she had known she would be.

In that small New England town, the trail goes cold. The family has moved again and the searcher cannot find anyone that can tell her where they went. She returns to the West Coast filled with frustration and sadness.

Her husband steps up to the plate and says that he will hire a law firm in the eastern state's capital to search for the young woman's family. He cautions his wife that the girl's adoptive parents must be protected from trauma in this process. They are in absolute accord as their efforts go forward.

After two months of expensive legal eagling, the adopted family's whereabouts is still a mystery. That effort ceases. The mother is told of an agency in the eastern city that specializes in finding birth parents and adopted children. It seems that children and parents in the adoption world have a powerful need to find one another, children especially, trying to find the answer to who am I really? or where did I come from? or why didn't they want me? or mothers, of course, what happened to my child? These questions, most profound to the essence of our need to belonging and to self-worth are so bedeviling to participants in adoption that a unique industry has been created to try and find the players in the drama.

The mother from the West Coast now places a phone call to such an agency in the eastern city she thinks might be central to where her daughter may live – she grew up nearby.

The mother begins with the flat statement that she wants to hire the agency – whatever the fee. She is asked specific questions. As she answers there is a pause between questions that gets longer and longer.

The man's voice becomes thicker. There is finally a very long pause. The mother asks if the man is still on the line. He is.

In a halting voice, the man tells her that the phone call he received just before this one was from her daughter hiring them to find her.

The mother calls her daughter and makes plans to fly east to meet her. The meeting is too emotional to put in words. Mother and daughter spend the week together. She sleeps on the couch in her daughter's apartment; after a couple of nights, they share her bed. They pour over pictures of the little girl growing up. High School, teams, proms, college friends, trips, so many with her beaming parents.

Near the end of the week, the two decide to share their magical renewal with the adoptive parents who have not been told of their daughter's yearning obsession to find her "birth mother." A phone call is made. The mother assures the parents there will be no interference in the family's life. The next day mother and daughter travel to the suburbs to meet her parents.

The parents are standing in the living room of the modest, neat-as-a-pin house, holding hands when their daughter and her mother breeze into the room. Their pictures of her at all stages of her life abound. Welcome is low toned and guarded. The daughter pauses in her joyous, effusive recitation of this miraculous reunion. Her father looks at her birth mother and asks, "What do you want?" His daughter is offended but the birth mother steps in and again assures the parents she does not want to disrupt the family. She congratulates the couple on the fine job they have done raising this wonderful young woman. She adds that she hopes they won't mind if she and the young woman become friends.

The West Coast mother extends her stay for another week. Her daughter gets another week off from work. They are inseparable. The mother brings her daughter to meet old friends. They share life experiences. They try to build a solid bridge to span the vacuum of the years.

The mother and her husband decide to invite the new member of the family to visit them. They will share their news with the children when their mother returns home.

Mother and daughter endure a wrenching farewell. They have truly bonded.

The mother returns home exhausted and exhilarated. She immediately tells her son and daughter about their new sister. The visit is planned for the Christmas holidays. In the months before the visit, new found mother and daughter are in almost daily communication – warm, cozy conversations and quick, intimate notes.

The new daughter arrives a few days before Christmas. She is introduced to her new "other family" in a blizzard of emotion. The next evening she is the star attraction at an elegant cocktail party attended by a large number of family friends, young and old. The mother is seeing a dream come true.

The new family sits somewhat self-consciously and solemnly for their Christmas dinner. The husband intones an emotional grace. When he concludes he asks the new member of the family is she would like to speak. She does. She looks at her mother and asks, "Why did you abandon me?" In the stunned silence, her anger continues to cut through the fabric of the life of everyone at the table. "Why did you leave me? How could you have done

149

such a terrible thing? I could have had all this. You took it away from me – why?"

Christmas and the new family are no more. The found daughter is deaf to all entreaties. She packs at once and leaves for the airport. Later attempts by the mother at reconciliation are coldly rebuffed. There has been no contact in years. The last letter sent to her is returned – addressee unknown.

# The Seeing Eye Dog

We live in the town of Chatham on Cape Cod. It was one of those sunny, almost summery late fall days that deceive us New Englanders. Polly pointed out a schedule in that morning's issue of the *Cape Cod Times* and suggested we drive up to the Cape Cod National Sea Shore Park in Orleans and go on one of their guided naturalist tours of Nauset Beach. We settled on a time and up we went.

Nauset Beach is a wonderful, long stretch of natural blonde sand that receives long rolling breakers from the Atlantic. It reaches some miles south, all the way to Chatham. The name comes from the Nauset Indians who dominated that area of the Cape. In fact, it is probably because of the Nausets that we are New Englanders and speak English.

The brilliant French mariner, explorer, and map-making genius Samuel de Champlain sailed along Nauset Beach in 1606 and anchored in what is now Stage Harbor in Chatham where he lost four or five men in a fight with the Nausets. He never returned.

There was an interesting team assembled by the National Park Service to define the plants and birds and tiny beasts of Nauset beach – a young woman ranger in her dark green uniform, an older man in a similar outfit. This man was blind and he had by his side a friendly black lab wearing the harness of a seeing-eye dog.

It was explained to us that the blind man was an expert on coastal ecology. His total blindness was apparently recent and his dog had just finished being trained.

We spent a pleasant couple of hours learning of the magic of things around us on a beach that we take for granted. In the course of this, we were mightily impressed with the knowledge and courage of the blind man. We were also less than impressed with his dog.

Most of us expressed surprise at the animal's lack of control. He seemed to be nothing more than a big frolicsome, friendly puppy. He frequently jumped up on folks, putting his two paws on their chest. His master obviously cared greatly for his helper but he was getting very little help. The dog was unlike any seeing eye dog we had ever seen. Polly and I wondered aloud about it as we drove home in the late afternoon gloaming.

The next morning I shuffled out to the driveway in my old slippers to pick up the morning papers. I happened to unfold the *Cape Cod Times* to scan the front page as I walked back to the house. One of the headlines stopped me in my tracks:

# Tragedy on Route 6A
### Blind man and dog killed on Highway

Retired professor at New York University and a volunteer guide for the National Park Service at the Nauset Seashore and his seeing eye dog were killed when struck by a car on Route 6A in Orleans last night.

The unidentified driver was not charged. He was transported to Cape Cod Hospital with chest pain after the accident. The driver told police that the man dressed in dark clothes and the black lab walked out of the darkness into the front of the car. Other drivers at the scene confirmed his story.

# Trapped

Charlie played football with me in college. He played tackle and was a pretty good player. In those days he was considered a big man. He was 6'4" and weighed about 240 pounds. He had every man's dream physique – narrow waist, broad shoulders. He was a good looking fellow with a kind of long, high cheek-boned face and close-cropped brown hair. He had a hearty laugh and liked to find occasions to demonstrate his good fellowship. Women liked him and he liked them. He came from a little town in Ohio and there was a small-town, unsophisticated charm about him.

After college, we both went into the Marines. In basic school we saw a bit of one another on liberty. We were social friends. He ended up in the artillery and I was in the infantry. We went to different parts of the world. I never did see him again. I was sorry to hear in Marine Corps scuttlebutt a couple of years later that he'd gotten into a jam over misplaced rounds that his battery fired. That was the last time I heard his name for over twenty years.

One day at the house, I answered the phone and a deep, raspy voice asked for Jack Warner. "You got him," I said.

"Jack," the supulchral voice intoned, "this is an old friend. We go back a long time."

I waited a while and searched my memory of voices. "Well, I'm sorry to tell you, I don't get your voice."

"It's Charlie, Jack." His voice was insistent.

"Charlie?" I paused again. I had no idea who Charlie was.

"Charlie." I made sure my voice reflected my puzzlement. He identified himself then.

"Well, Charlie," I said, "it's been years since I've heard your voice. We sure do go back a long time. How've you been?"

"Well, Jack," – God his voice was deep – "that's why I'm calling you. I've been having some problems and I need a friend." There were noticeable pauses between phrases. "I've always thought of you as a good friend, and I need help."

"What's the problem, Charlie?"

"I'm in a situation that makes it very difficult for me to get things done."

"Oh," I said, not understanding.

"I don't have freedom of movement, Jack. It's a hell of a problem."

Ah, I thought, he's in jail; in prison somewhere. What the hell had happened to him? I spoke my last thoughts aloud.

"What happened, Charlie?"

"It's kinda complicated. I met this girl when I got out of the Corps – didn't know her that well. Knocked her up – big mistake. We got married; she had the kid; we fought all the time. Got divorced. My life was up and down, then after a few years we got married again." He gave a rumble of a laugh. "Couldn't stay away from it."

I listened silently, wondering.

"But now I'm alone. She and the kid don't come to see me."

I was certain he was in jail.

"Where are you, Charlie?"

"Back in the old hometown. I didn't get very far. And now I can't."

"I don't understand, Charlie. What is it that restrains your movement?"

He rumbled again. "It's me, Jack. I weigh over five hundred pounds."

I was too stunned to respond.

"I'm in this little apartment. It's up a flight of stairs. I can't climb the stairs; I can't go down. I'm trapped here. I've got no job; I can't drive a car. I can't fit into the driver's seat – the steering wheel. I have a hell of a time just to get up to go to the head."

I think I said, "My God."

"I go on diets, I lose maybe a hundred, hundred-fifty pounds, then I put it back on . . . and more. The son-of-a-bitch who owns this apartment has thrown me out. I'm behind on the rent. If they take me out of here, I'm homeless. No money, no place to go – homeless. I need help, Jack. Can you send a check? I need money to keep going. I gotta pay the rent and my phone – it's always being turned off. I gotta have the phone. I order food with it, but if I had it full time I could look into doing some sort of a job – phone work"

This plea took a long time. His breathing was labored when he finished.

I asked him how much money he needed, wished him good luck, and sent him a check.

Some months later I was at a football game with some teammates from years ago. Charlie's name came up. We discussed his situation. As we talked, we slowly realized he had called everybody on the team. He must have used an old football program. He made his calls alphabetically. I got one of the last calls. A year or so later, I heard that Charlie had died.

# The Smell of Love

I have a friend whose wife died just about three years ago. They had many children and many, many good years, and he misses her greatly. This Thanksgiving Day he stopped at our house late in the afternoon to have a drink. "Do you remember," he said, "how Marie loved Thanksgiving?"

"I sure do," I said. "I remember the little packages of cranberry bread that she would give as Thanksgiving presents."

He said, "You know, I've had a funny thing happen to me the last two years on the night before Thanksgiving. Two years ago, around three o'clock in the morning I woke up and said to myself, 'Someone is in the kitchen. I can smell something cooking.' I got up and went out into the kitchen and the smell of cranberry bread baking was so strong that I opened the oven. Then I looked to see if a window was open and perhaps somebody at one of the houses around me was cooking. There were no open windows, and I went back to bed.

"Last night I woke up again. Same time. I could smell turkey. I was sure that somebody next door, one of the houses, was basting a turkey. You remember how I used to complain that Marie would set the clock for every three hours during the night and get up and baste the turkey? Well, I got up and went out into the kitchen, and, I'm telling you, that turkey might as well have been right there in the oven. The smell was that strong. I did the same thing. I looked at the windows to see if a window was open. Somebody was cooking – basting a turkey. Not a thing. The windows were closed and that turkey was being basted in my memory, I guess.

"I got back into bed and lay there staring at the ceiling."

Happy Thanksgiving, Marie.

# Safe at Home

A friend of mine was an umpire. He was a very good umpire. He worked in the best leagues in Western Mass and Connecticut. He turned down job offers to work in professional baseball, preferring to keep his full-time teaching job.

He was also a very good beer drinker and carouser with the boys. His wife, Lorraine, whose name he pronounced "Lo Rain" was often very upset with his post game, and no game, drinking and the very late hours they sometimes occasioned.

"Lo Rain" had quite a temper and when she lost it, bad things might happen.

One night, very late one night – early one morning – the umpire returned home. He removed his shoes at the back door. He tiptoed into the house, gliding gently in a slight weaving pattern in his stocking feet. He had taken a leak in the backyard so that he would not have the sound of water disturb "Lo Rain's" sleep. He slipped soundlessly into bed beside his sleeping wife. He lay on his back, not moving a muscle. He rationed his breathing.

He lay like that for what seemed a long time. There was a muffled explosion of sound. The quiet of the room was smashed. A grunt – arragh – the flat hard sound of something being hit – AHYRI – a cry of pain, "Oh, oh, my God, oh, oh, my hand."

The light was switched on. The umpire was lying in bed fully attired in his umpiring equipment: facemask, chest protector, jock with cup, shin guards. "Lo Rain" had hit the umpire in the facemask and had broken a bone in her hand.

# The Meanest Coach

My friend, Don McAuliffe, was an all-American football player at Michigan State. By just one vote he missed being awarded the Heisman Trophy which signifies being the best college player in America. Don's coach at Michigan State was the now legendary Biggie Munn. Having played some football myself, I know that some coaches can be mean. This little tale of Don's will tell you why I think Mr. Munn wins the meanest coach award.

Michigan State was playing Notre Dame at South Bend, Indiana. Michigan State had a powerful team, a roster loaded with outstanding players. They were one of the two or three best teams in America at the time. The third-string fullback was a sophomore from the tough steel town of Gary, Indiana. His name was Danny Polcharski. A large contingent of Polcharski's home-town fans had managed to get tickets for this big game. They watched Michigan State, led by McAuliffe, pound the Irish right there on their home turf. The gang from Gary, Indiana began to chant for their hero as Michigan State rolled up the score. "We want Polcharski. We want Polcharski. We want Polcharski." Their demand echoed around Notre Dame stadium. Finally, "Biggie" Munn turned to the bench and snapped, "Polcharski, warm up!" The pride of Gary put on his helmet and did some short sprints back and forth along the sideline while his fans cheered. Polcharski, their high school hero was going in against Notre Dame. Coach Munn turned to the eager fullback, "You ready?"

"I'm ready, coach."

"Okay, go up in the stands, they want you up there."

Polcharski quit the team on the spot.

He transferred to Purdue where he had to sit out a year before he would be eligible to play football. That following year, Michigan State had been undefeated for thirty straight games. Coach Munn's team was Number 1 in America. Purdue came to Michigan State to play them on a bright Saturday. Polcharski played fullback for Purdue. He ran the ball like a ferocious wild man. He dominated Michigan State. The final score: Purdue 6, Michigan State 0.

The lone touchdown was scored by Polcharski from Gary, Indiana.

Incidentally, Don McCauliffe has a bulldog – he calls him "Biggie."

# Do Bullies Always Win?

I have a theory that bullies always win. As I look at the world now, through the wrong end of the telescope, my theory is usually affirmed. It seems everywhere I look I see bullies triumphant: Wall Street, politics, sports, and nations.

I think now of an instance when I was wrong, and the memory stirs me on a chill winter night. I mentioned before that when I was young I raised chickens in a postage-stamp backyard, selling their eggs and occasionally chickens that I would decapitate to the thrill or revulsion of the kids in the neighborhood. These activities were aided and enhanced by my main job: delivering the evening newspaper – the *Springfield Daily News*. I was ten years old when I began these enterprises.

Years later I mentioned to my mother about what wonderful neighbors we had – "Those roosters crowing early every monrning and nobody said a word!" My mother looked at me expressionless and said, "Oh really?"

Most of my pals were paperboys. It was a six-day job. Papers were two cents when I started and jumped to three when the war came.

All the papers for our side of the river in Westfield were delivered to a gritty area in the back of a store owned by the Geehern family. The bundles came over in a truck from Springfield around 3:30 or 4:00 in the afternoon. We would go from school to the Y across the street from Geehern's, play intense basketball in our school clothes, then cross the street with our bikes and get our papers.

A big tough Polish kid – he must have been seventeen – was in charge of handing out the papers. There was not an ounce of fat or humor in the fellow. We'll call him "Ski." (I picked up this habit in the Marines; if you were Polish or had a long Eastern European sounding name, you were called "Ski.")

When you arrived in Ski's domain to collect your papers, you had to get in line and wait your turn. Stay too long playing basketball, scratch football, or whatever, and you were in the back of the line. First come, first serve.

Now, after all these years, I freely admit I could be a fresh-mouthy kid. One day I must have said or done something Ski didn't like and he made me wait until everyone else got their papers. "Okay," I thought, "once."

The next day he told me to go to the end of the line. I said, "No, I'm not moving. Give me my papers." I wouldn't move. He came out from behind the counter and we fought. Or rather, he beat me up – manhandled me. When he got tired of his exercise, he left me lying on the ground and went back to his position and doled out the papers. The other kids had watched all this in silence. I don't remember hearing anybody saying a single word.

The next day, the same sequence. Go to the end of the line – No – a fight.

Or my attempt at a fight. Ski was cruel and smart. He didn't mark up my face very much; but he was really punishing me; I had sizeable bruises on my body and a bit of a limp. When quizzed at home, I reluctantly told my folks that I got banged up playing scratch football. I didn't like that excuse because my folks were already letting me know they were not happy with the idea of my skinny body on the football field, but I certainly couldn't tell them the truth.

The beatings continued. Once in a while, I might score with a wild punch, elbow, or foot or finger, but I was now dreading going for my papers. Giving up the route never crossed my mind. I was really hurting now, physically and mentally. I would lie in bed at night and try to figure out the next day. I thought about bringing my baseball bat with me, but I was afraid I would end up losing that bat that I loved.

My brother Leonard was two years younger. He had no interest in paper routes, feeding chickens, or selling eggs. I drafted him to join me one day during Ski's assault on me. I had eggs to deliver

161

with the papers and Len would carry the eggs and a chicken in the basket of his bike and do the route with me.

My brother and I arrived back of Geehern's and by now everyone seemed to be in slow motion watching to see what the powerful Ski would do. We went through the usual routine, my little red-haired brother standing beside me…

"Back of the line!"

"No."

It was as though the other days had been practice. Ski was in a frenzy. He ended up straddling my body, hammering me. I remember a fearful hazy message in my mind: "He's going to kill me."

Suddenly Ski was not there. His ugly contorted face and his hammer hands were gone. He was gone. I turned my head. He was lying on his back. Blood was pouring from his head. My brother was standing with a brick in his hand. He had slammed the brick into Ski's head. The bully was unconscious for some time. He just lay there. No one moved. I remember a scary silence. I got up and took the brick from Len and tossed it. I can't remember what I said.

After a while, Ski moaned, I think perhaps vomited, and sat up.

It was the last time he tired to make me go to the end of the line.

On December 7, the war came. Ski was gone a few days later. He joined the Marines. In the late summer, news came to our neighborhood that one of the fellas in the Navy saw Ski being lifted onto a hospital ship off of Guadalcanal. It was in the paper that he got a medal.

I saw him some months later walking down Elm Street with his father. He had lost a lot of weight and his skin had a yellow cast to it. He looked sharp in his greens with his ribbons. Later I learned he was staying in the Corps, "going for thirty."

Years later, when I was in the Corps, I would once in a while wonder if I would bump into Ski. Now I had bars and he had stripes.  What would I do?  I determined I would try to show myself as a very squared-away Marine Corps officer and merit the salute I would expect.  I would also try to make sure he was not still a practicing bully.  I never did see Ski.

My brother and I were not close.  I think amiable but wary would define our relationship.  When Len was diagnosed with pancreatic cancer and the referee began the count on him, I drove up from the Cape frequently to be with him.  On what proved to be my last visit, I arranged to have some of his closest pals and teammates join me.  He was on a cot in his living room, being helped by Hospice and his ever-present family.  I was alone in the room with him after everyone awkwardly left.  As I said "So long," he asked me to come over to him.  He said, "I need to do something."

Len reached up.  "I want to give you a hug."

I bent down to him.  He made a heroic effort to hug me and whispered in my ear, "Have the casket closed."  I stood up and looked down at him and suddenly from way back came the memory of the little red-headed eight-year-old kid whacking the big bastard of bully with the brick.

# A Fine Romance

—thank you, Jerome Kern

In the 1970's I spent time in the Middle East, some of the time in Iran, in a place called Abadan, at the head of the Persian Gulf. It used to be, maybe still is, the site of the largest single oil refinery in the world. Abadan sits beside a river that is called the Arab-al-Shat. This waterway is the confluence of the mystical Tigris and Euphrates Rivers whose waters many believe nourished the crops and slaked the thirst of the people who began civilization. The Arab-al-Shat is also the boundary between Iran and Iraq.

The economic lifeblood of these two countries, both Muslim, one Arab and the other emphatically, proudly Persian, is the black gold that is pumped from beneath the desert.

It was because of this oil that after the First World War the wily British took a major position in the creation of Iraq and the stabilization of Iran under the rule of the shahs.

The British Army and their diplomatic nabobs learned to love polo in India – they brought the sport with them wherever they went. The Persians with their love of horses, which is almost religious, embraced the vigorous testing game.

It is because of polo that I have this story to tell.

When I was in Iran the British Army was gone; America now ruled through its pliant figurehead Shah Reza Pahlavi, King of Kings. I had an Iranian friend who was one of the bosses of the refinery at Abadan, a young, very bright engineer named Shahedi. This charming energetic fellow rode every day and was president of the polo club whose clubhouse was once upon a time the British Officers' Club and whose handsome horses were now stabled where British officers left their mounts.

One evening Shahedi and I were having drinks at the club and he told me that he had had a curious experience that day. He'd received a call from the army informing him that they had stopped a Frenchman at the Iraqi border who was traveling by horseback accompanied by a pack mule. The man's papers were in order and he was heading down to Abadan. He was planning to make a horseback trip around the world. He wanted to trade or buy a new horse. The army officer had given the Frenchman Shahedi's name, as head of the polo club. Shahedi expected to meet with him the next day.

The following day, as the ever overwhelming sun set across the river, I sat savoring an ice cold Heineken in the polo club bar and listened to Shahedi tell me about the wandering Frenchman.

Shahedi's dark eyes were sparkling as he talked and sipped a Pepsi Cola – Coke being forbidden in Iran, despite American protests, because Coke had unwisely built a large bottling plant in Israel. Shahedi had had quite a day; he was bubbling like his drink. Unlike me he was fluent in French, so he and the French cowboy had a lengthy conversation. Shahedi began to tell me and then stopped for a moment and said, "When I get finished with this story I have another one of great..." he searched for the word, "*coincidence*? Yes, great coincidence."

This is the first installment of Shahedi's tale.

"The Frenchman is a youngish fellow from Marseilles. He is a lawyer. He was well situated in a family firm. He said he went to lunch one day and asked himself what the hell he was doing with his life. He decided that he didn't like the answer so he did something about it. He decided that he would travel around the world on horseback. He loved to ride. He had a good horse. He would get himself a mule, load the mule with cooking and sleeping gear and some books he'd always wanted to read and head east – he never went back to his office."

He told Shahedi that his parents were stunned and his girlfriend very upset. So he told her that if she wanted to meet him he figured that he should reach the head of the Persian Gulf in about six months, so if she wanted to be with him he would look for her at the Caravansari Hotel in Abadan during a certain three days.

But he tells me he is quite late getting here because of problems that occurred in the Balkans.

"So what happens now?" I asked.

"Well, I like this Frenchman so I tell him I am going to take his horse – who is worn out – and we will furnish him with a good stout-hearted beast. I got the fellow a room at the guesthouse. I think he is as tired as his horse, which we stabled here. I arranged for another horse for him and I went back to my office."

Shahedi was an observant Moslem when he was in his homeland. We had been together in England and the South of France and I knew he enjoyed liquor but he seemed not to need the stimulus in Iran. Fortunately he didn't mind watching me drink; in fact, he signaled the waiter to bring me another superbly iced Heineken.

"Now we come to the coincidence, I guess," I said.

One learns very quickly in Iran that the people are Persians, they are not Arabs; they do not take kindly to being referred to as Arabs or lumped with the Arab world, but they most certainly have a storytelling tradition that mirrors that world. I'm sure the Persians would say the Arab world learned from them. Shahedi was wrapped in that historical verbal cloak now. I noticed that despite his engineering studies in Germany and France and his multi-fluency, his pleasure in his story caused him to add an *E* at the front of English words that began with an *S*. This was a habit I noticed in Persians who were working hard at their English. I think Shahedi was enjoying his storytelling role so much he forgot his linguistic sophistication.

He waited and set the scene with another Pepsi. "Well," he said, "I am in my office and I get a phone call from my friend who is in charge of the port. He tells me that there is a handsome young French woman who has been hanging around the port for some time. She was on a sailboat that sank in a storm off the Belaric Islands. The crew got picked up by a tanker and she is here, she was supposed to meet her lover in Abadan weeks ago but now she has given up on that and she is thinking now to take a job on one of the rigs in the Gulf. She seems to be a nice girl and his wife likes her and, of course, if she goes to live and work on a rig she will not come back the same woman. So his wife asked him to call me to see if I would have office work – she is very bright, also speaks English and German and he says he is sure she will learn Farsi.

"So I asked my friend," Shahedi said with a self-pleased air, *"Her boyfriend is riding horseback from France?* Of course, my friend is amazed I am knowing this so I bring him into the picture (a phrase beloved by Iranians) about our Cowboy as you call him."

I was appropriately impressed by this coincidence and the good luck of the lovers. "So what happens now?" I asked.

Shahedi smiled triumphantly. "I sent a car for the woman and had her brought to the guest house – tonight you and I are joining them for dinner at the Caravansari Hotel."

Before we go to meet the French Cowboy and his lady love for dinner, bear with me for a brief description of Iranian society at that time. The shah and the royal family and their supporting players – and that included key military men – were all filling their treasure chests with percentages of whatever business was generated from the black gold. Mostly the business seemed to be the United States selling arms to the Iranians which was akin to selling arms to ourselves since we had a great deal to say about how the country was governed.

Watching this dominance of their Moslem country by this most worldly Western power were what seemed to be a multitude of sullen mullahs – the turban covered clerics in the land of the Shiite sect of Islam. How unhappy these mullahs and their followers were with the American military dominance, the ubiquitous Yankees in their land, the uncovered ladies sipping cocktails in public restaurants, would be dramatically demonstrated in a few years.

Keeping the lid on these emotional people and their silent fury at the "Great Satan" in their midst and controlling other simmering

167

grievances were the shah's secret police who were so not secret that their name caused a shiver or a lowered voice or a quick turn of the head. They were called Savak. Their throats would be among the first to be cut in the coming revolution, but at that moment the knives were in their hands.

Now we are at the oil company's guest house meeting the travelers. The woman was attractive with short cut blond hair and a charming manner. The young lawyer – *voila!* – was a French cowboy featuring jeans, a Tom Mix type shirt, a bandana knotted at his neck and the pointed toes and distinctive heels of cowboy boots showing on his feet. He apparently did not speak a word of English. The young lady spoke English with a heavy liquid French accent.

At this time, there was very little to do in the town of Abadan – much more, however, than ten years later when Sadam Hussein invaded the place. There was a movie theater that showed films from Hollywood and Bollywood, which is India's film city. Shahedi told me the mullahs hated the place – I knew Shahedi loved the movies. I was told the place was always sold out. There were some small fly-filled joints where you could get scary food and strong drinks and there was the restaurant at the Caravansari which was as up the scale as the Iranians could get in Abadan. Tonight the place was jammed. We were obsequiously led to our reserved table which was at the edge of – surprise – a dance floor. We sat down and I heard the word *Champagne* used by the cowboy in speaking to Shahedi; that was fine with me. There was a band to go with the dance floor, outfitted in ill-fitting tuxedos and playing America's great gift to the world – Broadway show tunes. Two bottles of Veuve Clicquot – the Orange Widow – were brought to the table. Shahedi growled at the waiter in his soiled white jacket and he soon returned with a miraculous bucket of ice. The Cowboy opened one bottle and while he performed a nice pour into the wine glasses I looked around at the crowd.

Sitting in a far corner table were two splendid looking blondes with four black haired natives staring at them. "What's the story on the blondes?" I quietly asked Shahedi after the Cowboy had had us all touch glasses in a toast and was chatting with his lady love.

Shahedi lowered his head and his voice. "They are Swedes, they work on a Swedish tanker. The blonde girls must make more money on their visits to shore here than the tanker does carrying oil."

"Maybe they will write a book" I said. Shahedi looked surprised "How to become an oil millionaire on your back" I said. He burst into laughter. The French woman turned to speak to him, as she did the Cowboy got to his feet and faced her and executed a faint bow and extended his hand, clearly an invitation to dance. To my surprise – and his, I think – she shook her head *No*. The Cowboy gave a Gallic shrug. He turned away and stepped onto the dance floor and began to dance by himself – raising his arms, then holding them out like a bird in flight, spinning round, all quite fascinating and humorous.

A man worked his way across the dance floor. People gave him room when they saw him – rumpled dark suit, white shirt buttoned to the top, no necktie. He might as well have worn a sign – **Savak**. He tapped the Cowboy on the shoulder. They exchanged some words. He put a hand on the Cowboy's elbow, turned him toward our table and walked him a couple of steps. The Cowboy came back to the table apparently unconcerned, sat down, drank some Champagne and began chatting amiably with his lady friend while Shahedi and I conversed. He would give me snippets of interpretation of the lovers' very casual conversation. Despite the amazing chance of their reunion, the fellow seemed unconcerned by his lover's refusal to dance or be affectionate. One would never have guessed she had gone halfway around the world seeking him.

We drank Champagne and nibbled on tasty pistachio nuts, which have been a delicacy of Persian life for centuries. Shahedi ordered some hummus and we dipped into that. The music played

169

on. The waiter brought the very limited menu – another bottle of Champagne was ordered. " Just like London, eh Jack?" Shahedi was all smiles enjoying this bit of Persian pleasantry.

One of the blondes was dancing with a very awkward Iranian – probably his first Western dance, I thought, and wondered how many rials it was costing him

The Cowboy got to his feet; once again gave a slight bow to his lady and offered his hand and once again she declined. Shahedi and I exchanged puzzled looks. This was a strange love affair. I began to hum and search for the words to the Jerome Kern's ironic song "A Fine Romance."

The Cowboy sashayed back onto the dance floor and began a repeat of his solo number. Beside me I sensed Shahedi become uneasy. Sure enough the man from Savak was pushing his way through the crowd, this time followed by a couple of identically dressed assistants.

The Cowboy seemed ever more carried away with this performance, whirling, gliding and spinning. He was quite good. Many dancers had stopped or slowed and were watching him. The lead man from Savak tapped the Cowboy on the shoulder. He kept on dancing. Savak tapped again harder. The Cowboy spun and hit the man with the most explosive, coordinated punch I have ever seen. The man's feet went out from under him, he went down as though he had had a terrible backward slip on the ice. He was unconscious when his head hit the floor. Seconds after the punch landed, in a terrible moment, the repressed anger of Iranian society exploded. The two other Savak men were assaulted, one was wrestled to the floor and was being savaged by a couple who had been dancing. Other dancers were kicking at him. The other Savak was cowering from bottles that were hammering him. Fights broke out randomly – awful fights – I saw knives slashing, bottles broken to be used as cutters, tables overturned, chairs wielded. The band fled. The place was a scene of chaos – punching, kicking, noise, women screaming, men bellowing. It was a movie scene from hell.

I have been in some fights; some of them were quite mean. I had never seen anything like this. You could smell and feel a blood lust.

I shouted to Shahedi to take the girl and get out. I grabbed a champagne bottle by the neck, then pushed out to the Cowboy who was looking around the room with wide eyes. The Savak man was still flat on the floor. I jerked my thumb toward an exit. The French man stuck close behind me, a couple of times I used the bottle as a threat or a scythe. We got outside with a few bruises. My heart was hammering. I was wet with sweat. Shahedi was clearly terrified; the two French – the *causus belli* – were chatting amiably.

"We must get away at once," Shahedi croaked

"Let's drop them off at the guest house and get a drink at the club" I suggested. "You should get them out of here first thing in the morning, don't you think?" I added.

Shahedi nodded vigorously as he said, "Absolutely, absolutely!"

The next day. . . a Hollywood or Bollywood movie scene:

The stables and white fenced riding areas; very early morning, the sun just beginning to bake the mist off the river.

A mule with well-loaded back; two fine looking horses each with saddlebags and blanket rolls wrapped in ponchos.

One young lady in jeans and new boots with bandana on head.

One Cowboy in boots, jeans, cowboy shirt, bandana around neck, cowboy hat on head.

Lady and Cowboy bend down shake hands with Shahedi. I walk over and they repeat the act perfunctorily.

Cowboy leads his caravan out the gate.

They head up a small hill behind the stables, turn and wave. They are on their way to Afghanistan.

# The End of a Not So Fine Romance

America's hungry embrace of Iran and its oil fortunes came to an explosive end in 1978-79. This was a few years after my last visit. Many of us should have seen the storm coming. I found the Iranian people to be a perplexing mix of the modem and medieval, of the brilliant and facile, of bullheaded and furious, easy going warm affable hosts and suspicious, paranoid extremely volatile people who thought the Western World was looking down their nose at them while trying to steal their money. On that score they weren't paranoid.

When the marriage between the rulers of Iran and the capitalists of America ended, it was an explosive, savage divorce. In this case the principals walked off, or rather rushed off, with stuffed wallets while the children vented their murderous rage on one another. It was East against West, conservative Muslims bringing the wrath of their view of the Koran onto the heads of their sinful secular countrymen. Perhaps the most awful example of the barbaric punishment of the irreligious by the religious happened in Abadan. The movie theater, probably the most significant symbol of Western decadence, was an outrageous affront to the ultra-religious. They must have hated the sinners who were seduced by the celluloid enticements of another world.

One night after the Shah had fled and the country was in turmoil, the movie theater in Abadan was packed as usual – no doubt with folks who more than ever wanted to escape the real world. They failed.

A group of men came and bolted, boarded and barricaded the building. They set the theater on fire, incinerating over five hundred people.

Some years later I learned that Shahedi was at the movies that night.

"Nantucket's not as quiet
as they think."

—*Bob Ruley*

# Tourists

As I've said, I spent time in the Middle East, a difficult and dry place. When I had time, I would get away to a city and a country that I came to love – London, England.

When I was in London I would stay at the Dorchester or Brown's Hotel. I would revel in the muted, elegant, civilized ambiance of those places and the clean, orderly tempo of London. The contrast with the places I'd just left was dramatic.

When the evening got late after dinner, I would walk along Park Lane down towards the Duke of Wellington's house near Hyde Park Circle, where there was a place across from the Intercontinental Hotel that became my end-of-the-evening hangout.

The imposing building had been home of one of the Rothchilds. It was now an elite gambling club. The ground floor had one large room that had been fashioned into an elegant supper club. There was a cozy bar at one end of the room, many intimate booths and tables for dining on excellent food; the other end of the room had a small area for dancing and an alcove where a trio played great music – Cole Porter, Gershwin, Rogers & Hart, stuff I loved. They played long stretches and stayed late. I think the gamblers could try their luck all night, and they would occasionally walk down the wonderful curved stairway to dance or snack or relax at the bar.

The second floor was pure gambling. It consisted of one large room and three or four smaller rooms where you could try your luck at whatever. The place was very sophisticated. Many men wore tuxedos, and certainly all the help did. No women were under dressed, a good number wore evening gowns.

This was the height of the spending spree of the oil-rich Arabs.

There were always a number of Sheiks sashaying around. Most of them seemed to wear glasses, some dark glasses. I had learned that the Saudis in particular suffer from eye problems. It didn't keep them from having beautiful women – plural – in their company.

But it wasn't the sight or smell of money, the good music, or the comfortable bar that brought me so often to the club. I had made a friend there. It's nice to have a friend when you're alone in a big city that's not yours.

My friend was named Michael. Everyone at the club called him Michael; some called him Mr. Michael. I called him Mike.

Mike was from the town of Dingle in County Kerry in southwest Ireland, a place I knew well. And he grew up with people whose families I knew. The neighborhood I was raised in was thickly settled with people from that part of the world. That was the foundation for our relationship.

We always seemed to have plenty to talk about. I'd take a seat at the end of the bar – he'd move a chair there for me if there was none empty – and he'd stand and watch the room and chat with me while I sipped stingers on the rocks. He insisted that they always be "on the house." I never saw him chat with any other customer. He was quick and sharp-tongued with his associates. I never knew what the pecking order was, but clearly Michael was a boss. Every so often he'd excuse himself and move gracefully, in his finely tailored tuxedo, upstairs to the tables. In a few minutes he'd be back and pick up the thread of the conversation in his smoothed-down west of Ireland voice. The bartender kept one respectful eye on him, even when the bar was buzzing.

Despite his easy manner and pleasant conversation, this man of middling height and middling weight had a face that told you it had been a rough road he'd traveled to get to this elegant London club.

That Mike had been a prize fighter was obvious. That he'd been a good one was underscored by comments that others made. He told me he'd fought all over the British Isles and in Europe.

"A tough business," he said, "but not as tough as this one."

If I needed any nudging as to what the gambling world was about beneath the tuxedos and evening gowns, it came in the forms of two slicked-up savages who worked at the club and seemed to report to Mike.

One was a very big, door-filling Greek. His massive head had well-oiled black hair that was combed straight back from his forehead. There was a mean-looking red, fish-hook scar at one corner of his mouth. He wore his tux as though to the manor born. His demeanor with me was always cool and distant. He would favor me with a searching glance and nod. His associate – they were always together – was a small, wiry, balding Cockney with a pock-marked rat face and a steady thin-lipped smile that told me he was probably one of the nastiest bastards I'd ever met. His wearing a tuxedo was like putting a top hat on a crocodile.

Mike had never been to America. He had a sister who had left their village and was now living in the states, married with a family. He asked me if I knew where Somerville, Massachusetts was and was pleased when I said I knew it, just outside of Boston, and that I lived in the same state. I told him about Nantucket, where I lived. He said he'd always wanted to see America. I invited him to come stay with me. I could tell he was pleased by my offer.

Our relationship was very cordial. I'd always spend a number of late nights at the club when I was in London, sipping stingers on the rocks, talking about the world with Mike, and watching the intriguing gamblers come and go. I think he was impressed that I never gambled.

One evening after having been away from London for some time, I stopped in on my way to the Middle East. I asked the bartender if Mike was around. He gave me a quick look and said, "Michael's not here tonight." That was the first time I'd ever been there that Mike hadn't been keeping an eye on the place. I finished my drink and left.

I went back the next night and sat myself at the end of the bar. The bartender brought me a stinger and I looked around the room for a bit, hummed along with some of the music, waited a while, and then asked the bartender if Mike was around. He moved along the bar close to me, then put his head down low to cut some lemons. "Mike's gone," he said softly, with his head down.

"What do you mean *gone*?" I queried quietly.

"Gone, didn't show up, a couple of weeks ago. No one knows where he is. Gone."

He no sooner finished speaking than he moved away from me quickly to the other end of the bar. Before I had assimilated his news with the business of finishing my stinger, I realized I had company. The Greek and Rat Face moved into the bar, one on each side of me. The Greek did the talking and Rat Face did the smiling. First, would I have "another drink, Mr. Warner?" Sure I would. Wild horses couldn't have dragged me out of there right then. I was eager to see what they were going to have to say.

I noticed the bartender did not look at me – not even a glance – as he concocted and delivered my drink and immediately went to the other end of the bar.

The Greek was Mr. Conviviality. How was I? How were things in the states? Massachusetts, wasn't it? And, by the way, had I heard from our mutual friend, Michael?

He quizzed me on this score in a number of cute ways, and Rat Face watched me. I slowly but surely came to realize that Mike must have taken something belonging to the club when he left. And with no evidence whatsoever, I decided it was a lot of money. I grinned inwardly as I thought he must have been planning this move for years.

While the unsubtle quiz session was going on, a pencil-mustached man in a double-breasted suit that looked to me like cashmere came up to us. The two torpedoes came to attention and I was introduced as "Michael's American friend, Mr. Warner." The man's name was not given. I'd never seen him before. His hand was not offered. He spoke in a foreign accent. He said how much they missed Michael, hoped he was well, he understood I knew his family, perhaps I would have an address so they could reach his family and tell them how pleased they'd be to hear from Michael. I said I didn't know his family. Did I know where they lived? No I didn't. The man looked me over very carefully and left without another word.

Now I was certain that Mike must have hit these guys for a big number.

As they do always, in life, things changed. A year or so passed. I never went back to the gambling club. I was in the house in Nantucket on a day late in the spring – I guess May or early June. The phone rang. The voice was faintly familiar, "Jack Warner?"

"Yes."

"Is this the Jack Warner who used to visit a certain club in London?"

I knew the voice now.

"Yes it is, Mike."

"Ah – well done. How are you keeping?"

"Very well, and yourself?"

"Fine. I've been here visiting in a town outside of Boston. I wondered if you'd want to put up with a tourist for a night down there on that island of yours? Everyone tells me it's as nice as you said."

"Mike, I'd be delighted to have you visit. I'm here all the time for the next few weeks. Come on down any time. Call me and I'll pick you up at the ferry or the airport. It will be good to see you."

"You'll hear from me," he said, and hung up.

I think it was a Monday afternoon when I got that phone call. Around mid-day on Wednesday, there was a knock on the front door. When I opened the door, the big Greek and little Rat Face were standing there on my front porch.

I can't tell you what my first thoughts were. I know a jumble of things flashed through my mind as I took a breath and looked them over. I'm sure my face showed my – no, not surprise – amazement. The Greek gabbled smoothly about how he and his pal were just a couple of tourists seeing the sights in America and what an interesting place Nantucket is. I wondered – had they tapped my phone? Mike must have been visiting his sister in Somerville. Had they tapped her phone? How close were they to catching him? How did they figure me in this?

With a smoothness his face belied, the Greek asked, "Have you heard from our mutual friend, Michael?"

Two pair of eyes locked on me. "No, I haven't."

"He hasn't called or been in touch?"

"No." They knew Mike had called me. I was sure of it. But I wasn't sure of anything else.

They continued to stare at me. Rat Face never did speak.

We were at a crossroads right then. How tough would they get with me? How tough could they get with me here on Nantucket, U.S.A.?

What was the plot in this story?

The Greek squeezed out one more smile. "If you hear from Michael, tell him we'd like to see him." He turned and walked down the porch steps. Rat Face followed.

I stood watching them as they marched past the old Quaker houses of Main Street – a strange contrast of tranquility and savagery.

I never heard from Mike.

I don't know what the plot was.

# BWOOB

A fellow I know, a lawyer, was born with a condition that involved his testicles. One of them never, in the words of the doctors – never dropped. This circumstance did not bother him physically in any way. He was a fine athlete.

For a few summers, this fellow used to freeload at our Nantucket house for weeks at a time. He was a man who liked women and women liked him. But his relationships never seemed to last very long. He was on a constant quest for the perfect woman. Nantucket in the summer was the perfect place for him to search.

As time went on, it seemed that the perfect woman could not be found on Nantucket, so one day this fellow came to me and asked if I would write an ad for him that he would put in the personals column in a Boston paper. When I realized that he was serious, I agreed that I would do this for him. I wrote the ad as follows:

> Tall, good-looking attorney interested in sports, music, looking for someone to share his interests. BWOOB. If you come to learn what this means, our relationship will flourish.

The lawyer looked at the ad, and his first suggestion was that I change the word "good-looking" to "handsome." Then he looked at me and said, "What the hell does BWOOB mean?"

"Well," I said, it means, Born With Only One Ball."

The man ran the ad and received over sixty responses from the curious.

None of them proved to be the perfect woman.

# A Way with Women

I have a pal named Harry. He has always been the most attractive man to women I have ever known. To go into a bar where there were a number of women and have Harry by your side would give your ego an awful beating. His Latin looks, dark curly hair, fastidious clothes, and gentle manner made a powerful combination.

Women – young, old, beautiful, not so beautiful – wanted to be with Harry and were not shy about letting him know it. That was fine with Harry, but he always had his own private clock defining how much time he would give a particular woman because Harry wanted to make sure he had time for the other things he wanted.

Harry wanted time – often lots of it – in saloons, with cold beer and other guys, and other women, talking sports, making a few bets, maybe arranging to purchase something more stimulating than his beer. Harry's use of time did not include being a homebody.

Harry was married to June when we met. I never saw a great deal of her, but he and I became very good pals. We would drink beer and watch the Boston Celtics on television, back in the days when they were worth watching. I had heard rumors that June had left her husband and children and taken off with Harry. He never talked about that. June was older than he, and it was no secret that they had a rocky marriage.

He came to me one day and said he was moving out of the house and wondered if he could stay with me for a few days. I was divorced and had three kids living with me in a big house and I had plenty of room, so I said, "Okay."

One night after savoring a Celtics' game, Harry and I decided to go downtown for a nightcap. A pal of ours has a fine restaurant on India Street that has a nice little bar. Sitting at the bar that night were two young ladies. Strangely enough, one of them was named June. She was an airline stewardess who lived over on Cape Cod. Later I was to learn she was married.

Harry and this June, new June, hit it off faster than you can say the other months of the year.

She and Harry launched into an immediate passionate affair. So now Harry had two Junes on his calendar. After that night, he would disappear every few days and I learned he had the use of a small apartment downtown where he and his new June could relax. So Harry's time was pretty well full, what with trying to sell real estate, entertaining new June on her frequent visits, spending occasional nights at my house watching the Celtics, changing clothes and then disappearing again.

As time went on, when he was at the house there began to be a number of phone conversations that became more and more secretive and frequent. I had taken calls from both Junes looking for Harry. I figured he must be feeling some pressure, but to me and the world at large he showed nothing but his usual happy face.

The best way to learn about someone is to live with them. I learned two things about Harry that you could rely on. First, you could not rely on him to keep any kind of schedule; second, you could be sure that he would stay in bed in the morning as long as he could cook up a reason to excuse it.

With that last fact in mind, you can understand that I was surprised to look out of my bedroom window one Monday morning at six a.m. and see Harry backing his car out of the driveway. I wondered where he could be going.

Things happened rather quickly after that. On Tuesday the fellow who was the Island bookie came to the house. He was looking for Harry. He told me that the boys at the steamship said Harry left on the early morning boat on Monday. Did I know where he was going? When I said I was surprised and had no

182

idea, the man turned pale. "Jack, you know I take bets once in a while."

"I heard that."

"I took some huge bets from Harry. Huge for me anyway – on Sunday's football games."

"Really, Harry and I watched the games here in the sitting room."

"Well, he must'a died."

"Harry?"

"Yeah!"

"Not at all, he drank beer, told stories and seemed happy as a lark. He sure didn't seem like a man who was losing bets – big or little."

"Well, they were big, and he lost on every one. I lay off bets that big with guys in Boston. I haven't got the dough to pay those guys. I gotta find Harry. I gotta pay those guys. This is serious, Jack, you gotta tell me – where is he?"

Just looking at him, listening to him, I could almost smell his fear. I didn't know this guy well but he wasn't trying to hide anything from me. When I told him I couldn't help him, that I honestly didn't know where Harry was, he let out a big breath like he'd been punched.

"I gotta find him," he said. "Please, please, tell him to get in touch with me if you hear from him."

At the end of that week, I had some friends in for dinner. Two of my best pals – a doctor and his wife – were in the kitchen helping me get things ready for the other guests who were in the dining room. The phone rang. The doctor was closest to it and picked it up. When he said "hello," I turned toward him. His eyes widened and he spoke harshly into the phone, "What, what?... Wait a minute, wait a minute...."

He handed the phone to me. He looked very somber.

"You better take this."

I took the phone and spoke my usual, "Yes?"

"John Warner?" a loud voice shouted the question.

"Yes it is."

"Well, I'm gonna come over there and kill you. You son-of-a-bitch, you lousy bastard."

I must have taken a step back from the phone. My two friends obviously heard the shouting. They were staring at me with concern – not quite as acute as mine was.

The man continued to rant. "Hey, hold on, hold on," I said, "who is this?" I kept asking. He finally paused and I was able to get my voice in. "Mister, who are you? I don't know what your beef with me is. What are you talking about?"

"You don't? You lousy bastard. You steal my wife, ruin our marriage and sit over there, Mr. Bigshot. Well, I'm gonna get you."

"What's your name, mister?" I asked quickly.

"You know goddamn well what my name is, I'm June's husband. I see your phone number here on these bills." The thought raced through my mind, letting Harry stay at the house – no good deed goes unpunished.

"Listen, mister, you got the wrong guy. I've met your wife a few times, but I've never called your house and I have no relationship with your wife. You better ask her about this."

"My wife has thrown me out of the house. She wants a divorce. She told me she's in love with someone on Nantucket." He was shouting again. "I'm comin' over there."

"Well, it's not me you're looking for. There was someone staying here for a while, but he's not on the Island anymore. You better talk with your wife about this. I don't want any of this grief. I'm sorry about your troubles, but I'm not involved with them. Don't call here again."

"We'll see, you son-of-a-bitch, if you're lying, I'll get you. If it's the last thing I do, I'll get you."

The dinner party was not a rollicking success.

The next morning the phone rang. It was June from Cape Cod. A frantic, hysterical June. She told me in rushes and sobs she was sorry about her husband's call. He'd gone to their house last night after calling me and she told him her lover's name was

Harry. Now she must find Harry, she'd done what he told her to do and now he must come to her. Where was he? I told her I didn't know. She burst into tears.

"I've got to be with him. He's my life now. I did what he told me, now I can't find him." When I was silent, she spoke in a rush. "He told me to go home and tell my husband that I loved someone else, and then he said we could be together. Well, I did it, I told my husband. I'm here at the house waiting for Harry. I've been waiting here night and day. I haven't heard a word from him. When he calls or you see him, please, please tell him I called, I'm waiting. I don't want to stay on the line any longer now, he might be trying to call me." She spoke in between sobs. "I won't leave the house, I'll be here for him." She hung up.

Around noontime of the same day, the other June, Harry's wife, called and asked if she could come up to the house for a "chat." I said, "Okay."

I knew by her reputation that this June was a hard driving, successful businesswoman. In all matters she was tough and demanding. In all matters except one.

June and I didn't know one another well. We sat across from each other in the living room in rather wary silence for some moments. I was comparing her looks to the other June and came to no conclusion other than they didn't look at all alike – both attractive, but not show stoppers. Wife June was older than Harry and I figured at least ten or fifteen years older than the other June. June was rubbing her hands together, and finally she spoke. "I'm very uncomfortable, Jack. I don't like this, but I'm going to be completely honest with you. I want Harry back. Where is he?"

"I'll be just as honest with you, June, Harry left here without a word. I have no idea where he is and I'm getting tired of being asked. In fact, I'm tired of this whole damn thing."

"Do you think he's with that other girl?"

"I don't think so."

"That bookie, Paul, just left my house. He said he came here."

I nodded and she continued. "He also said some bad things

185

could happen if Harry's debts aren't paid right away."

"I expect that's true."

She looked coolly at me. During the entire conversation, she never lost that cool.

"I'm going to pay his gambling debts this afternoon."

"I guess Harry had a bad day with his football picks."

"He's had a lot of bad days – just to give you an idea, he owes for more than one bad day, but his football betting last week, just that day, the son-of-a-bitch lost $25,000 – trying to bail out his other debts, I suppose."

My face had to register my astonishment.

"That's right," she said. "He lost that in one day. It's awful, I know, and what's worse is I've been through things like this before with him, and I still want him back."

I guess I shrugged. There was nothing to say.

She looked down at her hands for what seemed like a long time. Then she looked across at me. "Has Harry ever told you about us? How we met and all that?"

"No, not a word."

"Well, I'm going to tell you."

For a moment her face looked like someone who couldn't swim getting ready to dive in the water. "I was married when I met Harry. I had three kids. We lived outside Boston. Our family went on a vacation to Cape Cod. We rented a house at a golf club for a month. My husband came down weekends. Harry was a bartender at the club. By the end of the month, Harry and I were madly in love. After the vacation, I used a girlfriend of mine as an excuse to go down to the Cape a few more times. It was magic. And Harry taught me to enjoy drugs – not heavy stuff, but it was a new, exciting life. I wanted it forever. I told Harry that. He told me to go home and tell my husband that I loved someone else and then we could be together." She stared right at me. "And you know, that's just what I did. I went home and I told my husband, and he went nuts and threw me out of the house, but this is Massachusetts and I got a lawyer, there were the kids, I was the mother, so my husband had to move out. I called Harry and told him. Then I didn't hear from him. I called the club. He'd left. They didn't know where he was. I was frantic. I wouldn't leave the house for fear I'd miss his call. I ordered groceries by taxi; I wouldn't stay on the phone with anyone, afraid I'd miss his call. Still I didn't hear from him. Finally, I hired a private detective to find him. He found him and I went to Harry and I told him I had done what he said. So we got married. I know this sounds crazy, but we did, and I want to keep him." She got up from her chair. "Can you believe that story, Jack?"

"Yes," I said. " Yes, I can."

# The Good Neighbor

When I was a kid, President Franklin D. Roosevelt used the phrase "Good Neighbor" in defining America's relationship with Latin America. The Good Neighbor policy caught people's fancy. The phrase stayed with us.

Long after FDR was gone, I lived the life of a single father on Nantucket for over fifteen years. Marriage was not one of my top priorities; in fact, it wasn't even on the list. I knew a fair – or unfair – number of nice women whose company I enjoyed, but not enough to discuss a lifetime partnership.

The truth is, I was quite content and I had good reason to think my cup was full. At one stage of my Nantucket life, I acquired a forty-two foot Bruno-Stillman fishing vessel and something in the neighborhood of five hundred lobster traps – some wire, some wood (there is more than a difference when you lift them). I became an offshore lobsterman.

I did it because it was an experience that I wanted. That experience was crowned when my oldest son decided to take a year off between high school and college and serve on the crew.

We fished 120 miles or so off Nantucket. Our trips involved at least one overnight. There were three of us on the boat, which was named *Semper Fi*.

There has been enough written about the commercial fisherman's life to fill a small library. I can tell you that I've done hard physical work, that I've been involved in some danger. To spend hour after hour balanced on a sometimes wildly shifting platform, lifting, emptying, baiting traps, piling traps on the stern for a move, lines whipping out from the deck around your feet captures your attention as much as any life experience. This is work that tests you in every way. I've often thought that only mining coal must be worse.

My son met every challenge and filled me with a pride that I still feel in my chest as I write these words. I remember rising in the old house at 129 Main at two in the morning, standing silently in the kitchen with my namesake, the two of us gulping our tea, then walking side-by-side through the gentle calm of Main Street, the most evocative street I have ever known.

I remember an afternoon at sea, hot sun, flat ocean. I was on the bow. We were crossing into that miracle of nature, the Gulf Stream, the water changing from a dark, brooding, opaque gray to a sharply defined, breath-taking clear blue. Suddenly, porpoises were visible, rising from the depths to leap in front of the bow. I called to Jack to give the wheel to the third man. My son and I lay on the bow, our heads extended, and watched the porpoises rise from that heavenly blue and play dodge 'em with the *Semper Fi*.

You can't buy that on Wall Street.

During my years on Nantucket, there was one question that you could bet on. You remember how it was with the question to Jesse Owens. This was a similar pattern.

Tell people you live on Nantucket and a curious look crosses their features. Without fail, they ask, "Really! What's it like in the off season?"

My answer would usually be brief: "I like it fine."

The truth was, I loved the off-season. I don't think there is any place as pleasant to the senses as Nantucket in the fall. The sun has a special quality. The moors abandon their drabness and acquire a dappled beauty. The stars in the night sky seem more clearly defined.

There is one last invasion of visitors on Columbus Day weekend, and then Islanders have time for themselves and their place and to be good neighbors.

For many Nantucketers, the fall means football – Nantucket Whalers football, led by the living-legend coach Vito Capizzo. My youngest son learned to love football and Vito at Nantucket

189

High School. It was a delight for me to watch Chris grow and become a successful student and athlete. He worked hard at all aspects of his school life and enjoyed football and basketball. I tried to be a silent presence at all his games – home and away.

The basketball team usually flew to their away games in small planes. I must admit, those trips in gusting, bitter, and sometimes squally winds, took some of the edge off of my contentment.

The off-season gives Nantucket folks time for one another. I had a few pals who met frequently at the end of the day in the kitchen at 129 Main. Good company, good stories, cold beer, and laughter. The wood-burning stove added warmth to the company. In the evening, Chris and I would watch the Boston Celtics and worship Larry Bird.

I knew that many of my contemporaries thought that by going to Nantucket I had quit on life after a divorce and a crushing experience in Massachusetts politics. In fact, when I turned my back on my past life, I discovered a new and more fundamental one. I thought that I had found that elusive element called contentment.

I met Polly when a college friend visited me on the island and I asked a wonderful Nantucket lady friend of mine to have dinner with us and to invite a friend to make it a foursome. She invited Polly who, it turned out, lived around the corner with her three small children. I had seen these handsome children with the small group that waited for the school bus at the Civil War Monument. I had never set eyes on their mother. We were practically neighbors. Then and there, at dinner that night, I decided to be a good neighbor.

I knew her ex-husband slightly, and the entire island knew his reputation as an ex-husband. He was frequently listed in the court news for stalking and harassing his ex-wife.

After meeting Polly, I reacted as men or boys do when they meet women or girls they are attracted to: I hoped to impress her.

Not too longer after we started to know one another, Polly had to move from the little house she was renting. For the legions of women raising their families with either no male support and/ or male harassment, I would imagine the phrase "you'll have to move" comes close to the "last straw" category. Polly's plate was full: three small children, a children's clothing store, and a very difficult ex-husband prowling the island. So having to move her little band to another rental would not be easy. However, sometimes adversity brings rewards, and in this case the reward was a wonderful 18th century captain's house in the town. The place fronted on one of the island's oldest streets and sat beside a worn, cobbled track. There was one problem – a big one. A small cat – a cat the kids loved and was forbidden in this house by the lease.

Polly rightly said that her children's lives were too disrupted as it was without being forced to give up the cat. She thought she could not rent the house. My advice was, "To hell with the lease. Swear the kids to secrecy, rent the house, and bring the cat with you." And that's what she did.

Across from the cobbled track that I mentioned, Polly acquired a new neighbor, a lady with a hyphenated name, a suspicious and narrow mind, and an ass that must have measured three axe handles wide. Charles Dickens would have recognized her immediately as trouble. Not too many hours after Polly moved her family into the captain's house, the hyphenated lady reported to someone (remember, Nantucket is a *small* island) that she was sure she saw a cat go in the house. She knew it was a violation of the lease.

So there I was, trying to be a good neighbor to this woman and giving her bad advice. Polly was sure that when the hyphenated lady could prove it, she would report to the owners that Polly had turned their lovely old homestead into a cat house. She and her little crew would be out on the street.

Polly had a high school girl as a babysitter. She would be there when the children came home from school and stay until Polly got home from work. A couple of days after the report of the hyphenated lady's suspicion, the high school girl came to the house, and when she walked into the kitchen she found the hyphenated lady standing there. The woman had enough sense to be mortified and disconcerted about being caught. She babbled about having seen something moving in the house and knowing no one was home, thought she should investigate. She hot-footed it out the door in mid-sentence.

Polly was both outraged and very worried. She was sure the woman had seen the cat and would call the landlord and have the family evicted, and perhaps trigger legal trouble. The hyphenated lady had Polly on the ropes.

A good neighbor ought to be able to handle this situation.

I got on the phone to the hyphenated lady and said I was making a neighborly call for Polly. I said that a very valuable collection of jewelry that Polly had inherited from her grandmother was missing. The lady had been found in the house by the babysitter. She must understand that she was the chief suspect. The insurance company had instructed Polly to call the FBI. The hyphenated lady could expect to be contacted and interviewed by the FBI. Polly was sorry that such a thing would happen between neighbors, but she must follow the directions of the FBI.

I waited a couple of days and then had a pal of mine call the "suspect" and tell her he was Inspector So-and-So, and he would be visiting the island sometime in the near future for a conversation with her regarding her role in the case of the missing jewelry.

The hyphenated lady caused no more trouble in the neighborhood.

Polly was impressed.

What more could a good neighbor do?

I want to thank President Roosevelt for the idea.

# Fluffy the Rabbit

This is a story about a big white rabbit who lived in Nantucket. We will call him Fluffy. Fluffy was loved by the three little Ramos children he lived with. Mommy and Daddy Ramos brought Fluffy home when he was a little bunny. The family and the neighbors watched in amazement as Fluffy grew into the biggest rabbit anyone had ever seen.

The next door neighbors' name was Martin. Mrs. Martin had four children and one very smart black sheepdog named Hero. The Ramos children and the Martin children played together every day. They loved to play with Fluffy who ran around the yard like an overgrown puppy. When Fluffy was out in the yard, Hero had to be tied up because he had made it clear he would like to chew on the big rabbit.

Fluffy got so big that Mr. Ramos built a nice house for him in the backyard. The house had legs on it so that it sat well off the ground. This was so Hero or any other dog could not harm Fluffy.

One bitter cold night, when the wind was slicing across Nantucket like a frozen scythe, Mrs. Martin let Hero out for his nightly run. Later the family heard strange muffled growling noises coming from the back porch. Mrs. Martin cautiously opened the door while her children gathered nervously, peering from behind her. There the Martin family saw Hero standing proudly with Fluffy the rabbit in his mouth. Mrs. Martin let out a cry and went out to the dog.

Fluffy was dead. His once pure white silky fur was matted with sand and gravel and blood. Mrs. Martin and her children were terribly upset. Their beloved dog Hero had done an awful thing. What could they do? What would they tell the Ramos family? The Ramos children were their best friends. Would they ever forgive Hero and the Martins?

Mrs. Martin thought quickly. She took Fluffy from Hero's mouth. She brought the rabbit into the bathroom and put him into the tub. The children gathered in awed silence and watched their mother. She washed Fluffy very gently, she took some liquid soap and cleaned up every bit of blood and sand. Then she got her hair dryer and used it to blow-dry the wet rabbit until he was Fluffy again. Mrs. Martin lined up her children in the kitchen. She made each of them promise that they would never, ever tell anyone about what had happened with Hero and Fluffy.

Mrs. Martin waited until all the lights were out in the Ramos house. She slipped out onto the back porch, down the steps and tiptoed through the bitter cold black night over to Fluffy's cage. She gently laid Fluffy down. She went home, put out the kitchen light and went upstairs to bed.

The next morning was Monday. Before the children went to school, Mrs. Martin reminded them of their vow of silence. Monday and Tuesday passed with not a word from the Ramos house. Wednesday morning Mrs. Martin went to the grocery store. Who should she bump into in one of the aisles but her good friend and neighbor, Mrs. Ramos. Her heart sank. What would happen now?

The two ladies smiled hello to one another and chatted for a moment. Then Mrs. Ramos said, "We had a very strange thing happen. We can't understand it."

Mrs. Martin was almost afraid to respond. "What happened?" she asked.

"Well," said Mrs. Ramos. "Fluffy died on Saturday. We didn't want the children to know, so my husband buried him in the back-yard. We told the children he ran away. Monday morning, after the children went to school, I was in the backyard and Fluffy was in his cage, all smooth and beautiful."

And that's the story of Fluffy the rabbit.

# How Does a Story Get Around?

Ever wonder how a story gets around? Who begins it? Makes it up? Or has it happen to them? And then, how does it travel? How do some stories get such fast legs?

Some years ago I was looking for a housekeeper/secretary on Nantucket. I wanted to downplay the housekeeping aspect of the job, figuring that vacuuming and dusting might narrow the field of talent. So I put an ad in the local newspaper called the *Inquirer and Mirror* that went like this:

WANTED –TO LIVE IN – SINGLE PERSON FOR LIGHT HOUSEKEEPING. SOME TYPING REQUIRED. FOOD PROVIDED. WAGES NEGOTIABLE.

The first call I got I thought was from one of my pals disguising his voice. "Where is the lighthouse?" the fellow asked. "And how long do you have to stay at one stretch?" After a couple of sharp "Who is this?" I finally realized this was not a jokester.

In the next four or five days, I received at least a half dozen phone calls asking the same question. It seems there are plenty of potential lighthouse keepers out there. I told my friends the story and we all had a chuckle.

In those days I used to watch the *Today* program in the morning. Big mustachioed Gene Shallit was a favorite of mine. Perhaps four or five weeks after I had the lighthouse experience, I was eating my cereal one morning, watching and listening to Mr. Shallit when he told the story of the fellow who put the ad in the paper looking for someone to do light housekeeping – and how everybody thought it was a lighthouse.

I stared at the TV set in complete surprise. My question, then, is still the same, how did that story of mine get from Nantucket to the *Today* program in New York in about four weeks? I never found out.

# The Star Boarder

The fellow you met earlier in a story called "BWOOB" was a frequent visitor at the house in Nantucket. For weeks on end – or rather, endless weeks – he would arrive for "a few days" in mid-June and leave around Labor Day. He became what my mother referred to as "the Star Boarder." He never needed a place to stay on Nantucket in the winter, but when spring turned into summer, he arrived – just like some birds. This went on for a number of years and, of course, it is another comment on my judgment.

Why did I put up with this? Well, as I look back on it, he was good company, to a point. We were both Celtic fanatics and he was a good backyard basketball player. In those days, I played a lot of backyard basketball. The fellow had a reasonable sense of humor but a staggering lack of sensibility in human relationships.

When he wasn't on Nantucket or working at his profession, he spent endless hours talking to psychiatrists. This therapy caused him to become a noisy believer in some doctor's theory that every blemish in relationships can be eliminated by full and frank discussion.

Over the course of a couple of summers, I became very good friends with a psychiatrist and his wife. They began coming to the island in August, along with about 10,000 other psychiatrists (I always thought that psychiatrists were lucky that Freud hadn't taken his vacations in February) and soon were spending every summer on the island. They were very pleasant, good conversationalists, and good company. They began spending lots of time at my house, and, of course, the Star Boarder was also there. You may recall from our earlier meeting with him, he was a tall, good looking fellow who liked lots of women and they liked him.

As time progressed, I realized that he and the psychiatrist's wife were becoming quite friendly. She mentioned to me that she had taken to writing to him during the winter, and I noticed that they were taking occasional walks out in the back meadow.

The woman made a comment to me one day that caused me to become concerned. I had become very good friends with her and her husband. We were having a dinner party at my house that night and I decided to have a frank talk with the Star Boarder before my friends arrived. I told him emphatically that I wanted no funny business between himself and the doctor's wife. And further, I gave him the ultimate threat of no more summer vacations on Nantucket at 129 Main Street if he disobeyed me.

Just before dinner started that night – after the cocktail hour – we ran out of ice. The Star Boarder was deputed to go get ice and the psychiatrist kindly went with him. They were gone a long time.

When they returned, the Star Boarder stayed in the kitchen and the psychiatrist came into the dining room and sat at the table. He looked a hundred years older than when he had left. An alarm bell went off in my head and I went into the kitchen. The Star Boarder was opening a bottle of wine. I asked him what took him so long to get the ice and he looked at me earnestly and said, "I decided I should have a talk with our friend the doc."

My heart sank.

"What did you say to him?"

"I got everything straightened out. I told him that his wife wants me to go to bed with her, but I'm definitely not going to do it and he shouldn't worry about it."

The Star Boarder left the next day.

# The Story of a Book
# that Never Was

*"Yesterday You Were My Prisoner..."*

# The Beginning of a Book
# That Never Was

This effort of putting words on paper was triggered by a comment made over drinks at a beachfront bar in Florida. My pals Jim and Dave Murphy were there with their sister-in-law, Paula, a lovely lady. I told a story and as the laughter subsided, Paula said, "That's a wonderful story. I'll bet you've got others. You've done some writing – I loved your book about Ireland. You ought to write some of your short stories." So here we are.

It's curious about writing. Lots of folks are planning to write – someday. But they find reasons that make someday no day. Among the reasons is one that I used to tell myself, or sell myself: first I had to make a living and then I would be able to spend time writing. Real writers, I think, will tell you this is absolute nonsense. Paycheck or no paycheck, real job or no job, writers write – no matter what, no matter where – they write. I wasted more time in my life with inconsequential grab-ass (a great Marine Corps word) than anyone else I know. But when the writing bug bites you, even a laggard like me will write.

I can remember writing on a notebook held on the transom in the wheelhouse of our lobster boat, standing with my legs braced while the Atlantic slammed us around. Moments like that tell you that you will write – must write. I learned though that sometimes events occur that can derail you off the heady track you are on.

My first published work was a novel called *The Loss of Heaven*. The story was about the tragedy of the Irish "troubles." The book received good reviews. Just as sales took off, the publisher went broke. I sold the film rights but I never made any real money.

200

Frankly, it didn't matter, despite the fact that it was late in the game, I was going to be a writer.

Two people who read *The Loss of Heaven* and had liked it were Jack Downey and his wife Audrey. I respect Jack as much as anyone I have ever known. Jack and I played football together in college. He was a fearless savage on the field, otherwise, a very bright, intellectual, fun-loving Irishman who would prove to be a patriot.

Jack was recruited by the CIA his senior year and had gone right into the agency. In 1952 he was stationed in Korea. Jack and a fellow agent were flown into China to pick up a Chinese Communist general who was going to defect. It was a trap. The crew of the plane were killed; Downey and his partner were taken prisoner. He would remain a prisoner until 1973. When he came home, he met and married Audrey Li, a Chinese girl who had grown up in the city of Shen Yang where he was first kept prisoner. Wrapped inside that paragraph is a remarkable story.

To my delight, Jack and Audrey Downey asked me to write his story. They had also decided they wanted to return to China for a visit – a decision that shocked or puzzled everyone who learned of it. They asked me to accompany them in order to get a better feel for the book. I agreed and I decided to bring my son Chris, who was thirteen at the time. The Downeys were in communication with the Chinese Embassy on all of this.

The results of that undertaking is another chapter that we will get to later. For now, I'll tell you the beginning of the Downey-Warner adventure. It begins with my notes of a meeting of Jack Downey, Vice President Bush, and President Ronald Reagan as Jack related it to me.

*Chinese ideograph for **prisoner** painted on all prisoners' clothing.*

## Yesterday You Were My Prisoner, Today You Are My Honored Guest

It is the summer of 1983. The two men moved along the smooth, cool, thick-carpeted corridor with the vigorous physical certainty that one often sees in former athletes. Men who still feel good about their bodies and their lives.

They are Yale men, had been, always would be. One, Mr. George Bush, the Vice President of the United States, still has the loose-limbed grace of his days as a Yale first baseman. His companion, another six-footer, is a rugged, square-shouldered man with a firm chin and what he likes to call a high forehead. He also has a smile that will reach inside you and will make you forget that he was a hard-nosed wrestler at Yale and a very tough guard on the football team. He is attorney John T. Downey of New Haven, Connecticut.

Outside, a mid-day August sun seems to have stunned the city of Washington, baking its buildings and forcing its citizens and visitors who are outside the genius of air conditioning to sweaty slow motion. For the visitor from Connecticut, the White House seems strangely apart from the heat and the lethargy. Jack Downey is very impressed with the feel of this place. It's more than the portraits, the solid furnishings, the sense of history – it's the people.

He has just finished lunch in the White House; the conversation of his hosts on matters foreign and domestic has been wide-ranging and thorough. Despite the fact that he is a steadfast Democrat, he has a real admiration for the sense of confidence and purpose of the people he has met here.

Of course, George Bush might have something to do with this. He is an eminently sensible man. A man who would be very hard to dislike. He has had more good jobs in government than any other contemporary American. Talking with him it is easy to see why. He is a calm, shrewd man with good instincts, and surprising for a political person, he is thoughtful.

It is George Bush's thoughtfulness that has brought Jack Downey to this corridor, heading for an impromptu chat with the President of the United States.

Bush, the quintessential Republican WASP, and Downey, the Irish Catholic Democrat, have more in common than a Yale degree. They both worked for the Central Intelligence Agency. And they have also both spent some time in China. George Bush was our Ambassador. Jack Downey spent twenty-one years in a Chinese prison as a captured spy – a CIA agent.

It is George Bush's thought that Ronald Reagan would like to meet Jack Downey and hear his story. Bush is a great fan of Jack Downey.

The corridor they walk ends at the waiting room to the Oval Office. There is a "Sorry, Mr. Vice President, he is in a meeting" response from the President's cordial secretary that is immediately cancelled by the appearance of a naval aide coming out of the door behind her. "I guess he's free now," the secretary says.

The Vice President takes Jack's arm and leads him into the Oval Office. The President is entering from a side door, adjusting his belt. He shows a hint of surprise at the sight of the two visitors. Surprise, not irritation. His eyes flick from Jack to George Bush who speaks now in a loud clear voice. "Mr. President, I thought you'd like to meet Jack Downey. This is the fellow I talked to you about. He was *the* Central Intelligence agent. He was captured in China, sentenced to life and spent over twenty years in prison there. Tell him your story, Jack."

Jack is sizing up Reagan, as the Vice President speaks. The President has a bright rose blush on his cheeks and his neck is wattled. These are the only signs of age in his appearance. He gives Jack's hand a good firm handshake and looks him over now with undisguised interest. "I'm sure glad to meet you. I'd like to hear about this China business."

It is a friendly request, one man to another. The President settles into a chair and motions to the two men to sit. Jack takes the cue from Bush and raises his usually soft voice. "I joined the agency my senior year in college, Mr. President."

"Yale," says Bush. And Reagan grins.

"I graduated in 1951," Jack continued, "went through parachute training, explosives, small arms, all that stuff, and was assigned to the Far East. Our mission was to train and drop anti-communist agents in Manchuria."

The President spoke up, "Chinese, of course?"

"Yes sir, they were supplied by Chiang Kai-shek's army on Taiwan. We trained them on Saipan and Okinawa. We hoped to set up a guerilla force up there in Manchuria that would harass the Chinese Communist Army that was putting so much pressure on us in Korea."

Jack felt there was no need to tell the President that the agents soon came to realize that their missions were suicidal. Or that there had been occasions when an agent had had to pull his pistol and push the unwilling agent out of the plane. The President had settled back in his chair and was watching Jack closely.

"We flew up to Northeast China," Jack continued, "to pick up a Chinese general. It was an ambush. The pilot and the co-pilot were killed."

"How'd they manage the ambush?" the President asked eagerly, a good storyteller listening to a good story.

"They had picked up every agent we'd dropped, Mr. President, and they started sending us phony radio messages."

"Wow," says Reagan. "So you went into China and got caught, huh?"

"Yes, sir. Myself and another fellow."

"And?"

"I spent over twenty years there in prison."

"Golly," says President Reagan. "What did they do to you? How'd they treat you?"

"Kinda tough at first, but later it was better." Jack has no intention of telling some of the brutal parts of his story to the President.

The Vice President speaks up: "Chains and shackles, Mr. President."

Ronald Reagan is a man who believes in heroes and loves heroics. He shook his head in admiration. "My God, that's gotta be some story."

"The first couple of years were the toughest, Mr. President. I was released in 1973 when President Nixon came to China. My mother was dying and they let me come home." Jack spoke in a voice that was lower now and the president had cocked his head.

The naval aide stuck his head in the door: "The committee is waiting, Mr. President."

Reagan shook his head and waved the man away. "No, no, not yet. I want to hear this."

He turned back to Jack with a question. "Where'd they keep you?'

"I spent most of the time in Peking. I had some Chinese cellmates, but most of the time I was in solitary." Jack does not want to shock the President by telling him that one of his Chinese cellmates probably died of starvation. "After the first few years I had some books."

"This is incredible," says Reagan. "I've never heard anything about this. How old were you when you were captured?"

"Twenty-two, Mr. President."

"Twenty-two, twenty-two..." The president's voice was loud. "And you were on a spy mission to China? God. Through all those years, didn't anybody do anything? Why didn't our people do something?" The president's voice was hard. He was staring at the Vice President. It was clear that Ronald Reagan would have done something. He wouldn't have let a young American patriot grow to middle age in a Chinese prison. He stared hard at George Bush. "Nobody here did anything, George? Why not?"

"Jack's situation was complicated for a number of people in our government, Mr. President."

"It doesn't sound that complicated to me, George. One of our boys – a hero – left in chains in China for over twenty years. That's awful."

"I'm afraid the best we could do was give him his back pay when he was released," Bush said.

"And the Internal Revenue took one-third of that right off the top," Jack said, with a laugh.

Reagan looked at Jack with astonishment. "My God," he said, and then he too burst into laughter as he shook his head.

The Vice President spoke into the last edge of the laughter: "Now Jack is planning a trip back to China, Mr. President."

"What?"

"Yes, sir."

"Why? Why would you go back? My God, I'd never go near the place if I'd been treated like you must have been." Reagan shook his head.

"Well, after all those years, Mr. President, I figure I've got quite an investment in China. It seemed to me that things had kind of been getting off the track between ourselves and China. I thought that my going back, my status as a former prisoner and all, might have some impact. I might act as a bridge of friendship between our country and the Chinese. It might help make all those years meaningful, make them worth something. My wife is Chinese, she was born there. She'd like to go back and see what things are like now."

Reagan stared at Jack with open surprise. "You have a Chinese wife? How did you meet her?"

"I met her in New Haven when I got home. She was working at the graduate school at Yale. We married when I was in law school."

206

"You came home and went to law school and married a Chinese girl."

"Yes sir. And we have a three-year-old son."

"Jack," the President was looking at Jack with what might be called amazement, "that is some story. And you're not afraid to go back?"

"No, sir. In fact, I'm looking forward to it."

The President rose and put out his hand. "I'm sure pleased to have met you. You're quite a guy. What a story you must have. I think your going back to China is amazing. It seems it can't do anything but help, do you agree, George?"

"I certainly do, Mr. President."

"Well, good luck to you and your wife on your trip," Reagan said. "It really is quite a thing going back there." He shook his head. "Gonna take your little boy?"

"Yes, sir."

The President smiled. "Ought to be some experience for him – for all of you."

There seems to have been a touch of every man about Ronald Reagan, a response to individual situations when he confronts them one-on-one that is instinctive and touches the nerve ends. A kind of bar-room basic. He asks questions that go to the guts of things. He immediately looks for the good guys and the bad guys. In his few minutes with Jack Downey he probed at the questions that seem to fascinate people about the Downey story. What was it like? Over twenty years in a Chinese prison, chains and shackles. Years and years in solitary. How could he stand it and come back to be the obviously squared-away man that he is?

The other big question has always been, why didn't the government of the United States of America do something about it? How could we have left him there? No American, in the service of his country, has ever been left in a foreign prison as long as Jack Downey was. Why didn't we get him out? These two questions jump at people who first hear about him and even now nag at those who helplessly waited for him from the time of

207

the Korean War to the Vietnam War. During Downey's years in Chinese prisons, we exchanged many top-level spies with our arch enemy Russia. Why not Downey in China? What was that all about?

Now, there's this business that really perplexes people: How could he ever go back to China? Why would he do it?

The press was advised of the meeting at the White House and the President and Vice President's approbation of the Downeys' planned trip to China. I knew it was important to Jack that he have his country's blessing for the trip. Some responses to the news that he might return to China bothered him. I thought they bothered him more than he would admit. The first was a *New York Times* editorial that pronounced that the *Times* felt that the Downey family's trip to China was a propaganda coup for the Chinese government, that Downey was being used by the Chinese. Then CBS called Jack and said that if he was going to return to China they would like to arrange a meeting in China between him and a fellow named Jim Minares and do a television piece about their meeting. Jack was appalled at the idea. He had heard Minares' name often in China. Minares was the last remaining American POW from the Korean War who was still in China because he chose to stay.

When the exchange of prisoners occurred in late 1953 at the end of the war, thousands of Chinese and North Koreans wanted to remain in South Korea. There was an intense diplomatic hassle about all this. The communists insisted that their people be returned – all of them. Hundreds and hundreds were forcibly sent back over the border to North Korea. Pictures and news of this created such a public uproar in America and Western Europe that over three thousand Chinese and North Koreans who absolutely refused to leave South Korea were allowed to stay.

America let Americans in communist captivity make their own choice. There were thousands of American prisoners; twenty-two Americans chose to stay in the hands of the Chinese and North Koreans. With typical communist disregard for the facts, this was turned into a major news story as a victory for the communist lifestyle. America was given a propaganda pasting by the communists world-wide because of the twenty-two who chose to stay behind. Jack had been peppered with stories of these men while he was in prison. He knew who Minares was – a turncoat. The last one left in China. There was no way Jack Downey would meet with this man.

Before the Chinese approval of the visit, there was a brief but very revealing face-saving two-step with the Chinese government that went like this: "If we invite you, will you come? And if you decide not to, will you not publicly reject our invitation?" This exchange made me realize the concept of "face" in dealing with the Chinese can never be underestimated.

This was all settled by Jack and Audrey announcing that they had accepted an invitation to visit China. They would bring their son and be accompanied by two family friends. They made it clear that they neither asked for nor would receive help from the Chinese with their expenses. However, we would be assisted in our travels in China by the Chinese Association for Friendship with Foreign Countries. This is the Chinese government's agency for dealing with foreign dignitaries who visit China. Through the good offices of a successful documentary writer/producer named Tony Potter, who planned to do a movie and a documentary from my book, we were also given quiet assistance on our trip by NBC.

So it was set. We would go to China. The year was 1983. Our group was a strange one. Audrey, Jacky and Jack Downey, my son Chris and myself.

Audrey Downey was born in Shen Yang, Manchuria, daughter of Dr. Li Shotung, who took his family from Manchuria to Peking steps ahead of the wave of Mao's avenging liberators. When Mao was master of all China, the Li family crossed the strait of Formosa to safety in Taiwan. Audrey was ten years old when she left China. She is now a handsome, high spirited woman, who loves her husband with pride and fierce loyalty. The light of their life is their very bright, very physical three-year-old son, John Lee "Jacky" Downey.

My son Chris is a 6'4"–175 pound fourteen year old sophomore at Nantucket High School. His youth and size will cause him to be the object of constant neck craning Chinese astonishment. NBC's *Today* program wanted to cover our trip but could not get a visa for their cameraman. The Chinese were very rigid on the matter of who would be allowed on this trip. There would be five of us, period. So it came that Chris would carry their equipment and serve very ably as their cameraman in China. And, as I recall, those cameras were not light. NBC would publicly praise him later on their *Today* program. My son proved to be an absolutely marvelous traveling companion, despite some very uncomfortable conditions that included an unnerving hospital stay for him.

The star attraction, Jack Downey, would be known all over China as "the spy who has become our friend." I had known Jack since football days at Yale. He had come to Yale from Choate where, as an Irish Catholic scholarship kid from New Britain, Connecticut, he was president of his class. At Yale he was as popular and respected as anyone on the campus. Always a leader, a fellow that men trusted. Yale in those days was a CIA recruiting center. Two college masters and one varsity coach ran the operation. They picked well when they picked Jack Downey. He would later be chosen Number 1 in his CIA training group. His patriotism and faith and the bizarre machinations of American political and business leaders combined to keep him in China under years of unbelievable pressure.

Jack Downey, his family, and the United States of America had been victims of three traps set by the Chinese. The first, when every agent that we had dropped into China had been captured almost when they hit the ground; the Chinese knew exactly what we were doing and when and had wrung the code words out of the agents so they were now communicating with the CIA. So, the Chinese had advance notice of the foolhardy, poorly planned flight into China by two young college men, neither of whom spoke a word of Chinese, to pick up a mythical Chinese general and take him out for conversations with the American military. Did the CIA assume no one was going to miss the commanding general of one of Mao's armies? And that they could then return him to Manchuria so that he could lead his armies against Mao? This foolhardy plan was in direct violation of National Security rules that agents who have broad knowledge of a strategic plan should never be placed in a situation where they might fall into enemy hands. Someone in the CIA should have gone to jail instead of Jack Downey. As things go in life, however, the people involved in this were promoted.

The second trap was the Chinese waiting for two years during which the United States government announced that Jack Downey was dead – lost on a flight between Korea and Japan – and paid his death benefits to his mother. This trap was sprung when the Chinese announced that Jack Downey was a spy working for Allen Dulles, brother of the Secretary of State, and head of the CIA. Downey had been captured inside China, and he and his fellow agent, Richard Fecteau, were alive and being held in a Chinese prison.

Now came furious denials by the United States, led by Secretary of State John Foster Dulles. He called the Chinese "liars, kidnappers, and international outlaws." He referred to the Chinese as "a nation of barbarians." Americans were outraged. In those days, no one doubted the word of our government. President Eisenhower ordered the Sixth Fleet to closely patrol and menace China's coast. At one point, it seemed that we might attack China over this kidnapping of these young Americans and the crew of a B-29 who were also being held illegally.

The third trap was sprung many months later after continued American abuse of the Chinese and denial of their allegations about Jack Downey. One morning, newspapers around the world featured photographs of Jack and Fecteau and a news release of the Chinese government quoting Jack Downey's and Fecteau's confessions at a trial held in Beijing. Jack had been sentenced to life in prison. His associate, Fecteau, was sentenced to twenty years. Chinese agents who had helped the CIA and who had been captured, had been saved by the Chinese for the trial and were shot.

The American government's response to all this was that this was a continuation of the Chinese government's barbaric brainwashing of two Americans who were civilian employees of the army and had been picked up from a plane crash at sea. We were most emphatic that these men were not CIA operatives.


By the time we left New York on the flight to Tokyo and Beijing, the media had grabbed hold of the return to China story. *The New York Times* apparently lost its fear of being a propaganda tool for the Chinese Government and ran a couple of stories. One piece had two pictures of Jack, one in the prison uniform he was wearing when he was released from China into Hong Kong, the other is in his lawyer's uniform. The three major television networks have invited the Downeys to come and tell their story. Newspapers from all over America are calling Jack's house or law office. To my chagrin a famous writer has contacted Jack about doing a book about his life.

To prove how long ago this was, we flew on an airline called Pan American. They were terrific, giving us first class accommodations and celebrity treatment on the long, long flight across the Pacific. Even as they minister to us, the question doesn't go away. At various times three different stewardesses, and finally the pilot himself, sidle up to me in the soft light of the cabin and, as though they had the same drama coach, they glanced sidewise across the plane to where Jack was sitting, then lowered their heads and quietly asked if I could explain to them why Jack was going back to China "after all that has happened." My response got fuzzier and fuzzier until I finally settled on, "I'm not sure, I'm just a pal along for the ride."

During our stop in Tokyo, there was intense, controlled concern – a steady buzz – between our plane crew and Japanese officials. One of the stewardesses told me in confidence that the Korean Airline plane with the ironic James Bond number 007 that had left Kennedy three or four minutes after us and flown in very close pattern with us across the Pacific had broken off a conversation with our pilot in mid sentence. This occured soon after 007 angled off en route for its destination of Beijing.

Jack had a brief meeting with the press in the Tokyo airport while the plane and passengers prepared to resume the journey to the still somewhat forbidden middle kingdom we call China.

Audrey, Jacky Downey and Chris were asleep as the plane left Tokyo and headed north to China. Jack and I sat together and he talked. The trip was opening floodgates of memory. He talked randomly of his years in prison, of one of the few Chinese cellmates he had, "Uncle," a former police chief of Shanghai under the nationalists, whose ambition had been to be a cowboy. Uncle was against the communists because he was sure they wouldn't let him keep his two wives. It was Uncle who wrapped his arms around Jack and calmed him when he broke one day and taunted the guards to shoot him, shouted at them, "Shoot me! Shoot me!"

In a very low voice, he spoke of watching Uncle starve to death during the three-year famine China experienced during the 60's. He talked of "Miss," the precise, cold-blooded, multi-lingual warden/interpreter who was later humiliated herself and turned into a draft animal during the Cultural Revolution. The memories were sharp and poignant. His years in solitary seemed to cause his memory to be one of total recall.

He remembered with delight and fondness the first conversations with Americans after two years immobilized in shackles and chains, and interrogated night and day. He had had neither soap nor water through all that time, and was still in the clothes he had been captured in. Jack had borrowed a pair of fur-lined flight boots against the bitter cold for his trip into China. They were too tight and caused an infected toe that had gone untreated. He had made a young man's decision to wear his Yale letter sweater under the flight jacket as an extra layer of clothing. This announcement to the Chinese that he had gone to Yale caused them to believe, right to the very end, that he had been sent directly from the White House to spy in China.

Now suddenly he was placed in a tunnel cell with other Americans. A B-29 crew. He learned then that the Korean War was over – had been for eighteen months. He remembered these men with fondness and some with great respect. A Major Baumer, missing part of a foot and most of the fingers on both hands, stumbling, falling, in anguish and pain as he crawled on his way to the latrine on the icy floor of the prison. There were no crutches for Major Baumer, but no complaints and steadfast religious faith.

He spoke of Col. John Knox Arnold, commanding officer of the B-29 squadron, whom he met once briefly when he was brought out of solitary to pose for propaganda pictures. A man whose arms were popped out of his shoulder sockets in order to force him to sign a confession. A brave man, badly treated by his government on his return to America.

Most of all, Jack talked of a flying officer from Tennessee named John Woodrow Buck. A man with a marvelous mixture of humor and toughness. He told the Chinese in the early part of his captivity in Manchuria, "You people consider yourselves a great nation. Well, why don't you prove it? Do the right thing. Shoot us. Don't keep treating us like this. This is a disgrace. You ought to be ashamed of yourselves. Get this over with like decent human beings." Jack recalled Buck and his songs – one of defiance and one of yearning. The defiance song signified to the men that they might be down but they were not out. They might be tiny pawns in the uncountable hands of the Chinese, but they were still full of fight and spirit. John Woodrow Buck had taught them the song in his down-home Tennessee twang when it seemed like some of the crew were becoming overwhelmed by the situation. He would say, "Boys, let's sing to the guards about that little ol' mouse from Tennessee." And he would begin:

The beer was spilled on the barroom floor
The bar was closed for the night
A little ol' mouse climbed out of his hole
And sat right down in the light.

He lapped up the beer from the barroom floor
And back on his haunches he sat
And all night long you could hear him shout,
"Bring on that God damned cat!"

By the time they got to the end, the cave-like cell would be rattling with their voices, in a loud, bold challenge to the guards, to China, to fate. "Bring on that God damned cat."

The B-29 crew had been stationed in the Philipines. Their usual mission was dropping guerilla agents into North China. They said they had been on a leaflet dropping mission over North Korea when they were shot down, but their plane and parachutes had carried them into China. Now the crew was together again after almost two years of harsh treatment. The airmen were sure this meant they were going to be set free. Their going-home song was an old Louisiana song called "Jambalaya" that they had adapted to their Philipine connection.

Crawfish pie, jambalaya, fillet gumbo
Son of a gun, have big fun in the barrio
Good bye, Joe, I gotta go, me oh my oh

At Christmastime in 1955, as they sang that song, the intensity of their desire filled the tunnel. That Christmas was still a sweet memory in Jack's long nightmare. He spoke of a can of Spam, the long, long time he spent eating it. His first meat in over two years. The good fellowship that warmed him from his American comrades. He spoke of John Buck saying to him late one night, as he talked in his down-home country voice, that the awful part of this prison experience with the Chinese was that they took away your manhood. "John Buck was right," Jack said, "and through the years it never changed. Every time you thought you had reached the lowest point imaginable, they would strip away another layer of your self-respect and humiliate you in another way."

A stewardess leaned over us and spoke in a gentle voice, "Mr. Downey, the pilot thought you'd like to know we have just entered

Chinese air space." Jack smiled at her and turned and stared out the window. Suddenly the black sky exploded in a series of spectacular streaks of lightening. It was the most awesome night exploding, sky-ripping slashings of the darkness I had ever seen. I shivered a bit and wondered if China was the right place to be with Jack Downey. He turned from the window. "Quite a welcome," he said.

We were met in the airport in Beijing (Why is it China keeps changing the Western spelling of the Chinese language? In my lifetime this huge city has been Peiping, Peking and Beijing.) by a tangle of Chinese and Western newsmen. Their questions echoed around the cavernous reception hall. The key question seemed to be the same one that President Reagan, NBC's Bryant Gumble, American newspaper people, Connecticut politicians, and Pan Am folks had asked: Why was Jack Downey returning to China?

No one asked Audrey's reasons. They were obvious. She was met by a group of laughing, sobbing relatives, some of whom lifted their eyes up quickly from time to time to study her American husband in a less than inscrutable manner. Her aunt and uncle are physicians in Beijing. They too seemed to be fascinated by Jack.

The representatives of the Chinese People's Association for Friendship with Foreign Countries pushed through the crowd and introduced themselves. Mr. Yao-thin, quiet and intense. He seemed to be a gentle man but I sensed steel beneath the surface. He would later tell me about growing up in Shanghai where his parents were child laborers, about the bitter cold winter week in Shanghai when the bodies of five dead children were taken from the crowded, unheated building that his family lived in. In my conversations with him it was clear that his credentials as a future Chinese communist leader are impeccable. It will be interesting to see if he surfaces in the hierarchy in the years ahead.

There was Mrs. Du – a lovely, intelligent, olive skinned woman. And finally, Mr. Qu, pronounced Chu, who would be a pleasant, hard working, constant companion on our journey through China. The endless rhyming possibilities of Chu gave Jack, Chris and me

216

lots of amusing opportunity for impromptu songs and poems in his honor during our trip. His favorite seemed to be a song that ended with us chorusing the line, "There's no one but you, you, you, Mr. Chu!"

A comfortable, Japanese-built van was waiting for us. Mr. Yao chatted with me on the long ride through the night to the newly built Fragrant Hill Hotel. It was a soft, warm night. Despite the fact that it was well after midnight, there were occasional cyclists or horse-drawn carts moving silently along the dark edge of the tree-lined roads. Mr. Yao sat beside me and explained that it is Chinese law that each citizen, regardless of age or status, must plant five trees every year. Eventually China will have marvelous forests, he said. Then he began to talk about America. He has visited twice. It was obvious that our country fascinated him. His voice had a sibilant, hypnotic quality. His English was excellent. I noticed that he paused almost imperceptibly on his L words.

He was aware that I planned a book about Jack – obviously the Chinese Embassy had done their homework. He wondered if I intended to touch on the impact that former Secretary of State John Foster Dulles had on Chinese-American relations during Jack's first years in prison. He was pleased when I told him that I hoped to dig deeply into the Dulles record because I believed that Dulles' rigid mind-set on the matter of Red China had disastrous consequences for Jack Downey and America, perhaps setting us on the path to Vietnam.

Yao nodded agreement. I would soon learn that there were no Dulles fans in China. Yao mentioned that former Deputy Foreign Minister, Ambassador, Central Committee member, and Secretary to Mao, Wang Bignan was President of the Friendship Association. Mr. Yao said he hoped that the seventy-seven year old diplomat's health would allow him to have dinner with us. I hoped so too. He would be a wonderful source of information as to what the Chinese government's view was of the Jack Downey story and I hoped would confirm research I had done as to why

217

America had let Jack spend so many precious years in a Chinese prison.

Mr. Yao told me that he was delighted to be able to meet Jack Downey. He said that Jack is well known to the Chinese and they are fascinated with his return to China. Yao lowered his voice and leaned toward me. "Tell me, Mr. Warner," he said softly, "we know that Mr. Downey suffered greatly in his years here. After all that happened, why has Mr. Downey come back to China?" I was just barely able to suppress a laugh as we pulled up to the entrance of our hotel.

There was no laughter in the lobby of the Fragrant Hill Hotel. It was a scene that each one of us fends off into our subconscious hell. The Bible refers to the weeping and gnashing of teeth – there was all of that and screaming and pounding on walls. There was uncontrolled grief. A madness of sadness. Never believe that Orientals are inscrutable.

These were relatives and friends waiting for passengers on Korean Air Flight 007. They had just been told that the Russian government had announced that the Russian Air Force had destroyed a Korean commercial aircraft for violating Soviet airspace. The plane was Flight 007. All 269 passengers were dead.

Jack and I sat late in the bar trying to make sense of this random barbarism. Or was it random? Strange as it sounds as I write this now, we wondered if he figured into this massacre. Russia certainly did not want to watch Jack Downey begin sketching the outline of friendship between China and America. We had been told our plane was very close to 007. Had the Russians shot down the wrong plane? My mind was in a whirl as I trudged down one of the long, long corridors of the Fragrant Hill Hotel.

When I entered our room, Chris was lying in bed with the lights still on and a book in his hands. When I was ready for bed, I asked him if it was okay to turn out the light and he said, "Yes." I kissed him good night and turned out the light. After a few minutes Chris' voice came to me in the quiet: "Dad, do you think they shot down the wrong plane?"

"I don't know, Chris," I said. "Jack and I were just talking about that. It's a strange, savage piece of business. God help those poor people."

The next morning, Mr. Yao joined us for breakfast. No one had said a word about this, but there was no doubt in my mind that Mr. Yao was a major player in Chinese security. He very politely asked if he could join us at the table. Jacky Downey was fussing and Audrey was giving him her full attention. Mr. Yao declined offers of food and then said quietly, "I have come to tell you that Wang Bignan is prepared to meet you for dinner this evening." With that, Audrey swung round in her chair and stared at her husband. This was big news. I guessed that of all the things that Jack Downey might have hoped for in China, a meeting with someone of the stature of Wang Bignan must have been at the top of the list.

Our first day in Beijing was a strange admixture of events. That morning we were taken to a steel mill. This place could only be well defined by Dante himself. We were issued cotton gauze face masks when we went into the factory. You could feel the grit, dirt, and dust in the air with your hands. It was hard to notice the few workers who did wear masks since the masks were black. It was also difficult to notice any workers who seemed to be moving with any kind of haste. The place looked like a communist/socialist description of a worker's nightmare in some capitalist state. It was a dreadful place that certainly wouldn't have been allowed anyplace in the Western world.

A doctor friend of mine once told me that China, because of industrial accidents, is the great teaching ground for orthopedic surgeons who wish to acquire the skill of taking people's large toes off and turning them into thumbs. Watching the workers' risk taking, even in their slow motion in this mill, would have been breathtaking if we had dared take a deep breath. We couldn't get out of that dreadful place fast enough and when we did, our masks were black, despite our brief visit.

We stood outside and listened to Mr. Chu reel off endless

statistics of the Chinese people's ability to produce the hardware of modern life.

After a long, delightful lunch in what seemed to be downtown Beijing, our hosts made what I thought was the strange choice of taking us to the zoo. The Chinese are hugely proud of the panda, and I expect this was the reason for their decision and the object of most eyes were the pandas. They deserved the attention. There were a number of them and they are a delight to watch – playful, intelligent, roly-poly performers. They were in an open-air setting that gave them a big stage and they made full use of it. As we watched the pandas, we were soon nearly surrounded by Western and Chinese press and photo people who were sticking close to Jack, Audrey, and Jacky. Now I understood that the zoo was a photo opportunity for the Chinese government to display the friendly relationship with "the spy who has become our friend."

Mr. Chu, Jacky, Chris and I escaped the press and wandered through the crowded, cavernous building that held the big cats. There was a Siberian Tiger that was the most impressive animal in size, bearing and ferociousness that I had ever seen. His roaring had the other animals prowling nervously in their cages. It seemed that the latent power in him made every other animal in the place uneasy. Later, as we straggled back to our van, I asked Jack what he thought of the massive tiger. "I didn't go in there," he said.

"You didn't?" I started to speak further, and I looked at him and I stopped. He was unusually serious. Suddenly I understood. "Oh," I said, "of course."

"Yeah," Jack said. "You got it. I don't want to watch anything, any living thing in a cage."

Through much of this curious first day in China, I thought about Jack's mother, Mary Downey. I had done a good bit of research about her before we left. She died a few years after Jack was released by the Chinese. I felt as though I knew Mrs. Downey. She reminded me so much of my own mother. I wondered what she would think of this trip.

I knew that her son got his wonderful qualities of constancy and steadfastness and religious faith from his mother because I had become a huge fan of Mary Downey. She was a widowed woman with three children, teaching school in New Britain, Connecticut, whose patriotic son, it seemed to me, had been abandoned by the powers that made American foreign policy. After being notified by the government that her son was missing and presumed dead in a plane crash flying from Korea to Japan, and defining him as a United States Army employee, Mary Downey refused to believe that her son was dead. When she received the insurance death benefit, she bought a cemetery plot but would not have a Mass said because she still refused to believe that her son was dead.

Two years later, when the Chinese sprang their announcement of Jack's capture, Mrs. Downey began a battle for Jack's release. Ironically, this battle was not just with the Chinese government; it was with her own government. They rebuffed her and she fought back, and never ceased fighting.

There was no place and no one that she wouldn't go to to plead her son's case. She had allies. One, U.S. Senator Tom Dodd of Connecticut, father of the present Senator, fought for her and pleaded her case wherever and whenever he could and he took her case to the highest levels of American government. It seemed to me, he had been everything we hope for in an elected citizen.

Another rock helping to protect her from the tempest that life had brought her was the pastor of her parish church, St. Maurice's, Fr. Anthony Murphy. Before we left for China, I had spent a fascinating day in conversation with this calm, thoughtful intellectual priest at his retirement house in the lovely town of Norfolk, Connecticut. He had been a friend and counselor to Mary Downey through the agony of the long, long years of her son's imprisonment.

When I left my meeting with Father, now Monsignor, Murphy, the slim, intense, white-haired gentleman walked me to the door and said something to me that would later haunt me.

Much of the information I had gathered I had not yet shared with Jack since I was trying to put it all in coherent form and thought it could best be done after the trip when I assembled a manuscript. But I had been nagged by the same question that Ronald Reagan asked: Why? Why did America let Jack Downey spend those endless years in a Chinese prison? Prior to our trip, and after my conversation with Monsignor Murphy, I had the great good fortune of talking with two other gentlemen who shared personal experiences with me that shed a powerful light into that murky question.

One man I never met. I was referred to him by an erudite pal who said he might be a good source of Downey information. The man's name was Townsend Hoopes. He was a retired international correspondent for the Associated Press and the author of a book entitled *The Devil and John Foster Dulles*. He extended me the courtesy of a lengthy phone conversation.

Mr. Hoopes covered the United Nations for many years and had become a close friend of Secretary General Dag Hammarskjold. Mr. Hoopes told me that he was pleased to get my call because he had been holding information on the Downey matter for years and had not known quite what to do with it. He had been given the information by Secretary General Hammarskjold, but sworn to secrecy. Now Hammarskjold was dead, Downey was back in America, and he felt free to share his information with me and the public in the book I told him I was working on.

Townsend Hoopes remained a good reporter. He gave me his story in an orderly, concise manner. He reviewed the opening scenario in the Downey story: America announcing Downey's death on a supposed flight from Korea to Japan, the Chinese waiting over two years then announcing Downey was a prisoner who had been captured as a spy, and then waiting and baiting the United States into our vigorous, roaring denials of the Chinese claims with Secretary of State Dulles defining China as a "godless, barbarous nation." Hoopes made the point that with the power pair of John Foster Dulles as Secretary of State and his brother Allen, head of the CIA, most of the world's diplomats and political leaders wondered just what was going on in the conduct of United States foreign affairs. Particularly when, in response to the Chinese announcement of the Downey capture, the powerful American Sixth Fleet was ordered to patrol in close to the Chinese shore. Was America going to war over this affair? Then he recounted the shock when the Chinese played their ace: Downey's confession and his sentence to life in prison. He mentioned that it was around this time that America coined a new word that became part of the Cold War: *brainwashed*.

Mr. Hoopes said he had considerable evidence that the Secretary of State had constantly nagged his brother to set up an effective guerilla army inside China that might trigger a civil war and give America an opportunity to aid the anti-communist guerillas and help drive the communists from power.

Hoopes said that a year or so after the Chinese final public announcement in the Downey affair, Hammarskjold went to China and met with China's powerful Number 2: suave, sophisticated Chou En Lai. Hammarskjold told Hoopes that no one he had ever met on the world scene had impressed him as much as this Chinese leader. He said that when he brought up the matter of Downey and the other American prisoners, Chou En Lai's response flabbergasted him. (From what I've read of the Swedish diplomat, it must have been a rare thing for him.) Chou's response was simple and stunning. Three things must occur. One: the United States must admit that Downey and his associate were inside Chinese territory on a spy mission. Two: their parents must be allowed to come to China and take the prisoners home. Three: the United States must allow the news media to come into China.

If the reader could imagine the relationship between America and China at that time, and the harsh bitter language used by our State Department in defining the People's Republic, they would understand why the Secretary General was amazed by this offer.

Hoopes told me that Hammarskjold contacted the State

Department as soon as he returned to America. He spoke with the Secretary of State and recounted Chou's terms. The Chinese offer was flatly rejected. Dulles called it "blackmail." Hammarskjold said he was as bothered by this exchange as anything that ever happened to him in his diplomatic career. Hoopes, speaking for himself, said that he thought Dulles' attitude to the Chinese, as the lead Asian agents of the Communist devil, was our first step down the slippery slope to Vietnam.

A friend of mine was the second gentleman who was able to substantiate part of Chou En Lai's offer to America. His name was Bill Dwight, Sr. He was publisher of the Holyoke, Massachusetts *Transcript* and once a partner of mine in the ownership of a weekly newspaper. Bill Dwight was president of the American Newspaper Publishers Association, an outspoken, go-through guy. By a stroke of great good luck, I reached out to Bill and asked if he had any knowledge of the story of China offering to open its doors to American newsmen. Not only did he have information, he had had a personal meeting with Secretary of State Dulles to push the issue. Bill wrote me a lengthy letter recounting his meeting with Dulles. I don't think any of Bill's reporters ever had a bigger scoop, but it was a story that couldn't be told. Bill's letter is before me now; it is a masterful reporting job.

Information had leaked, as it certainly should have, that the Chinese had made an offer to the United States to open themselves to scrutiny by the American press. The American Newspaper Publishers Association was one that John Foster Dulles could not cold shoulder, so a meeting was set up with the Secretary of State to discuss what would have been a sea change in our relationship with China. Present at the meeting on Bill's side of the table was Russ Wiggins, then editor of the *Washington Post*. Bill and Wiggins were greeted by former Governor of Massachusetts, and then Undersecretary of State, Chris Herter. Bill figured that Dulles was playing on the Dwight–Herter, Massachusetts–Republican comradeship. After a bit of small talk, Bill Dwight and Russ

Wiggins were stunned when the Secretary of State walked into the room with Henry Luce, founder, chairman, grand panjandrum of Time Life, Fortune, etc. Luce and his publications had essentially enforced America's diplomatic line with China since 1939. Luce had been born in China of missionary parents and he was sure he knew what was best for America in dealing with China. He was an anti-communist, Chiang Kai-shek man to the end of his days. He was certainly a central figure in establishing the antagonism between America and Communist China. His spirit lives on in today's unsettled, muddled relationship with China, Taiwan and America.

Bill Dwight said that Dulles controlled the meeting from beginning to end. To Dwight and Wiggins' surprise, the Secretary of State acknowledged that indeed there had been an offer by Chou En Lai to allow American newsmen into China. But he said of course this was a trap. American newsmen would be used to spread propaganda for the Communist Chinese. China would use America's press to become part of the "family of nations," and this must never happen. He even, as Bill said, got personal when he mentioned the family that owned the newspaper in his hometown of Watertown, New York, saying that no doubt they'd turn a trip to China into a junket with their wives and become seduced by Chinese food and drink. When Dulles was through, he asked Luce to comment, and to the astonishment of the two newspaper men, Henry Luce, the leading newsman in America, agreed with Dulles that the American press should not be allowed to go to China. "Look at their behavior," he said. "They are trying to blackmail us using these illegally held captives. Communist China must remain a pariah in the world."

The fact that this meeting was held is being made public now for the first time.

So ended Chou En Lai's attempt to build a bridge to America. It did not end Mary Downey's attempt to free her son.

• • •

225

Mrs. Downey had tried on a number of occasions, with Senator Dodd's help, to talk with the Secretary of State. He declined with letters bemoaning the "outrageous illegal imprisonment of your son by the Chinese government." He never had the guts to meet with the mother of one of these captives. Ironically, his boss, President Dwight Eisenhower, apparently was not made of such cold material, and on three occasions he did meet with Mary Downey. All he had to offer was sympathy. Jack's boss, Allen Dulles, head of the CIA, never acknowledged any communication from Mrs. Downey.

At Father Murphy's suggestion, she had gone to see Cardinal Spellman in New York. Spellman was the Catholic Vicar of the United States Armed Forces and a man who always beat a loud patriotic drum. The priest had accompanied her on her trip to New York. The monsignor said, sadly, that Spellmen received them with what he would almost define as contempt. Did Mrs. Downey not understand that her son was a government employee and must take his chances like all government employees? When Mrs. Downey asked him why America was willing to trade other prisoners and not her son, and that her son was only twenty-one years old when he signed on with the government, Spellman responded, "He took his chances like we all do, Mrs. Downey. You should understand that," and got up and left the room.

In her twenty years of pleading for her son, Mary Downey begged for help from some of America's top officials. Monsignor Murphy told me that when John Kennedy was elected President, "Mary and I were elated." Here was the sympathetic power ear she needed to talk to. Here was an Irish Catholic patriot who would certainly understand that her son's patriotic assessment had been paid in full. Here were some of her own who would be appalled by the fact that the United States was allowing her son to be kept captive in a Chinese prison.

Connecticut people had been out in front in the Kennedy march to victory. A meeting to make her case with the sensitive new President certainly should be possible. Connecticut Democrats and Republicans close to the Kennedys went to work.

The President would not see Mrs. Downey; his brother Robert would handle the matter.

The monsignor said Mrs. Downey's meeting with Robert Kennedy was one of the lowest moments in her never-ending search for help because her expectations had been so high. Kennedy obviously cared. He made a point of letting Mary Downey know that he was aware that Jack had gone to Choate – the Presidents's school. He embodied the warmth and grace she had expected from the cardinal. Despite his attempt at personal kindness, his answer to her plea was a firm "No." Monsignor Murphy said that Mrs. Downey left the meeting with Robert Kennedy in the depth of despair. If the Irish Catholic Kennedys would not help, who would? Who could she turn to?

In too short a time, she would find Lyndon Johnson's people just as immovable.

I'd like to take a minute to comment on the reason for Mrs. Downey's sad and unrewarding trek through these Democratic administrations. I think what happened here was a simple case of lack of political nerve. Another trap had been set for Jack Downey. This time by the Republicans for the Democrats. Dulles and Luce had made antagonism to Red China a condition of American foreign policy written in stone. Anyone who ignored or tried to upset this policy, anyone who thought it might be helpful to make a gesture to bring China into this curiously named "family of nations," would be immediately branded as "soft on Communism." No Democratic administration would dare help Jack Downey. The heavy hands of Dulles and Luce were still on the tiller, directing our China policy. It's also why Johnson, when the awful truth of Vietnam was staring him in the face, could not say "Stop." The Republican Nixon could open the door to China. His party had closed it; they could unlatch it.

There was, however, one major international figure who put himself on the line for Mary Downey. Monsignor Murphy told me that through the good offices of Senator Dodd, Mary Downey had met with Secretary General Hammarskjold in New York. Dodd had learned that the Secretary was headed for a meeting in China and suggested that Mrs. Downey meet with him and ask him to intercede for her with the Chinese. The Monsignor said that Mrs. Downey asked him to accompany her, but he said to me, with a thin smile, that he declined, telling Mary, "You will be better off with the church out of this business with the U.N."

Mary Downey took the train to New York and met with the Secretary General. The widowed school teacher now had a record of meeting a goodly number of important people in her effort to free her son. She said she was sorry the priest hadn't accompanied her because there was a religious quality about Hammarskjold that touched her. He was the antithesis of Scandinavian coolness. He treated Mary Downey with great warmth and courtesy. He said he would do whatever he could for her cause in his meetings in China and would contact her on his return. She told Father Murphy that Hammerskjold impressed her more than any person she ever met.

Hammarskjold was as good as his word. When he returned to America, his office called and invited Jack's mother to New York. That next conversation with the Secretary General must have stunned Mary Downey. He spoke to her with great kindness and said that it must never be known that the suggestion that he was going to make to her came from him. He advised Mrs. Downey to go to China and ask to see her son. He said it might help her cause.

Mary Downey well knew that at that time Americans were not allowed to travel to China. We had put up our own diplomatic iron curtain between America and the world's most populous nation. Hammarskjold told her that "Your government will probably try to stop you, but they'll be afraid not to let you go."

And that's just what happened. Despite private warnings and threats from strange men who visited her house and calls from faceless officials warning that she would lose her citizenship if she defied United States law, telling her that if she went to China she would not be allowed to return to America, Mary Downey went to China. In fact, over the twenty-one years, she visited China three times to see her son.

Each visit must have been bittersweet agony for mother and son. I know that Jack was never given any indication that his mother was in China. He would be taken out of solitary – wondering, perhaps worrying, and brought into a room – to find his mother standing there. When I try to imagine this experience, my emotions fill me.

Ironically, fate intervened in America's fulfilling the three Chinese requirements for Downey's release. President Richard Nixon realized that only a Republican could get away with establishing a *rapprochment* with China. When Nixon shocked the world by flying to China to meet with Chinese leaders, and was accompanied by American newsmen, he was asked a pre-arranged question in his first few minutes on China's soil.

"Mr. President, what about the case of John Downey?"

"Well," Nixon responded, "Mr. Downey was an operative of the Central Intelligence Agency and we will discuss this matter with Chinese officials. His mother is terribly ill in a hospital back in Connecticut and we would like to get Mr. Downey back with her as soon as possible."

So after all those years, we gave the Chinese the admission they had asked for and let our news people take a close look at China. But Mary Downey was not able to be with her son on his trip home.


Now, we were about to have dinner with Wang Bignan. Through all the years of America ignoring China, the only semi-official government contact between the two nations was in their embassy in Poland. Wang Bignan, among his other jobs as Mao's Secretary and Foreign Minister, had frequently held the post of Ambassador to Poland. In all of these roles, the Downey name would be familiar to him. Jack and Audrey were also well aware that they were meeting one of the last members of the power elite that had transformed China into a communist monolith. This was a big event for them and for me. I hoped to get confirmation of the stories I had been told of Chou En Lai's outreach to America and how our country's reaction had effected the life of John T. Downey and others.

A private room on the upper floor of a Beijing restaurant was the scene of our dinner. There was a bit of trouble in getting Jacky ready on time for this event, so we arrived a few minutes late. Our group consisted of Yao, Chu, Mrs. Du, the Downeys, my son Chris, and myself. The adults were well aware of the impropriety of being late for this significant meeting and I think we were all a bit on edge. There were three men in the room when we arrived. It was immediately obvious which one was Wang; the other two men seemed anonymous in his presence. A palpable sense of power emanated from the small, bald, dark-skinned man. His head seemed to sit right on his shoulders as he watched us from half-lidded eyes, like a wise old turtle – a snapping turtle. Wang and his two aides were dressed in the plain, button-at-the-throat Mao jacket that all Chinese officials once wore. However, Wang's outfit was a tan color of obviously richer material – I thought it was silk. Mr. Yao, who acted as interpreter for the only time during our visit, was wearing a Western business suit and tie as was Mr. Chu.

Wang Bignan rose with some difficulty and extended both hands in a gracious gesture to the Downeys. His voice was deep, guttural, harsh. He spoke Chinese throughout the evening. Later we learned that he spoke German and French fluently and understood English very well.

"Mr. Downey," he said, "we finally meet. I first heard your

230

name in Warsaw in August, 1955. Mr. Alexis Johnson, your Ambassador to Poland, brought up your name. I continued to hear your name in various places for over twenty years. Mr. Downey, you are famous."

The meal was excellent, a half dozen courses of somewhat mysterious items that were all delicious. Wang asked how we liked the Fragrant Hill Hotel and before we could answer, he spoke in English with scorn of the hotel and derided the service.

"Cost number one," he said, "service number ten."

He was right. Jack had told me of this tactic of self-criticism which we heard in many of our meetings with the Chinese. He called it preemptive self-criticism and said it is a favorite ploy of the Chinese that he learned in his endless hours of re-education. The Fragrant Hill Hotel is supposed to be a showplace. I. M. Pei, the well known Chinese American architect, designed the building, but the interior plan is wretched. It is about a fifteen-minute walk from the elevator to our rooms. But none of us want to engage in a discussion of contemporary Chinese building. We had more important things on our minds. Jack and Audrey knew I was going to ask Wang some questions about Jack's prison years. I decided to ask at once about Wang's view on the Dulles-China story. He seemed prepared and pleased to tell the Chinese version.

First, Wang discussed an event that has become part of Chinese folklore, an historic moment that has become legend in China. Like all legends, the clarity of the facts are fuzzy. It is the story of the Secretary of State of the United States, John Foster Dulles, insulting the Premier of China, the revered Chou En Lai. One thing became clear in the first few days of our visit: the stoic, enduring Chinese people were frightened by the savage excesses they discovered within themselves during the Cultural Revolution. Probably because of Audrey's presence, we learned that everyone had a story about those unbalanced years when the Chinese people suffered a kind of national nervous breakdown. In listening to details of events of that time, one sensed a deep misgiving and well controlled resentment at Mao – the great helmsman who lost

231

his way and took a billion people with him. Chou En Lai, the smooth, careful and perhaps sensitive number two man, is known to have been appalled by the Cultural Revolution. He is now clearly first in the historical affection of his countrymen. Thus the story of Dulles' treatment of Chou has probably grown in parallel with the esteem of the Chinese people for their premier.

The snubbing of Chou occurred at the Geneva Conference held in 1954, a meeting of western nations, called by the French and including Russia and China, to discuss the civil war that had begun in what was then known as French Indo-China, and is now and will be forever known to Americans as Vietnam. Dulles had not wanted Americans to attend this conference because the Chinese would be there and his policy was to prevent communist China from entering "the world family of nations." Finally, reluctantly the United States agreed to take part. It is a tenet of Chinese belief that in Geneva, Dulles turned his back on the outstretched hand of friendship of Chou En Lai, literally turned on his heel and walked away. Wang's memory for events at the conference seemed very clear and precise. His recollection is somewhat less dramatic than the popular Chinese version, but it is nevertheless a recitation of a policy of continual studied insults and rejection of Chinese leaders on the part of the United States delegation. The Chinese learned, Wang says, through the Russian Foreign Minister, Molotov, that Dulles had issued firm instructions to the American group that they were not to acknowledge the presence of the Chinese in any way. These orders included specifically that no American was to go so far as to shake hands with any Chinese delegate, especially the major Chinese figure at the conference, Chou En Lai. Wang noted that he accompanied Chou as his assistant.

"In the same car together, every day," Mr. Yao said quietly to me, with awe in his voice.

Whenever Wang mentioned Chou, a kind of reverential nodding approval was the reaction of the Chinese at the table. Wang said the closest the Chinese got to conversation, formal or informal, with any American was in a restaurant with Under Secretary of State, General Walter Bedell Smith, Eisenhower's war time chief of staff. Wang recalled Smith being cordial and said that perhaps if he hadn't had a drink in one hand and a cigarette in another, Smith might well have shaken hands. Wang said that Dulles refused to even look at the Chinese during the conference and that only a brave soldier like Smith would have the courage to defy Dulles and chat briefly with Chou. He went on to talk of Dulles' unshakable belief that Russia and China were one. "What a mistake that was," Wang said. "People should know that China is China, she is no one's lackey. I know that at Geneva Chou hoped that an accommodation could be reached between our two countries. A great opportunity was missed at that time."

For a few minutes we wandered conversationally through the now leafless historical thickets of the 50's. Finally, it was time to find out the Chinese version of what America was doing about the young man from Connecticut, who, in the winter of 1954, was being kept in bitter cold solitary somewhere in this city. A young man who would spend over twenty-one years in cells where the light was never turned off. The man who was now sitting here, deftly using his chopsticks with his eyes riveted on the old warrior-diplomat. I asked Wang if he recalled the offer made by Chou En Lai to release American prisoners held in China if American and Chinese newsmen could be allowed to visit one another's countries. He does indeed. Also he adds, looking directly at Jack, "Your country was asked to acknowledge why you were in China, and Chou En Lai wished for your parents to come to China for you. Your mother did come here to visit you, I believe."

Jack nodded, stone faced.

Chou's offer, Wang says, was made late in the year 1955 to U. N. Secretary General Dag Hammarskjold. China was willing to swap the prisoners for one reason, he says: "To improve relations with the United States. This was Chou's goal. We knew what Mr. Dulles had been trying to do to our country but we wanted friendship. Chou believed friendship with America was very important. The prisoners would be released on this basis."

"Did that mean all American prisoners?" I asked Wang pointedly. "Would everyone be sent home?"

A meal in China is an active affair. There is continuous motion. Suddenly, the busy eaters around the table paused. There was a moment of silence, hands were still. Wang Bignan did not look at Jack. He spoke a rough, short phrase, tearing into the quiet of the room.

"Absolutely," Mr. Yao translated. "All American prisoners would have been sent home, everyone."

I looked at Jack Downey. His face was pale but expressionless. At that moment, I felt that I could read his thoughts. It was at that time in 1955 that he was spending his time with the B-29 crew who were sure they were all going home. It was the time of songs – the only time in China for Jack. He spent three weeks with the crew, then suddenly he was taken away and put back in solitary. The crew was released the following summer. Jack would be kept in China for seventeen more years.

Conversation was desultory after the recitation of Dulles' rejection of Chou's offer. Finally, Wang Bignan rose to this feet and raised a small porcelain cup filled with maoti, the savage colorless Chinese liquor.

"I offer you an old Chinese toast," he said, through the interpreter. "I believe it is very fitting." He looked straight at Jack and said, "Yesterday you were my prisoner, today you are my honored guest."


Jack Downey had worked to arrange an exchange program of books and, hopefully, students, between the Yale Law School and the recently reopened Wu Han University Law School. So the next destination on our journey was in the sprawling city of Wu Han on the bank of the Yangtze River.

At this time in China's historical development, Deng Xiao Peng was now the 4'11" master of the Communist apparatus and of the people it stood upon. In one of history's many ironies, this little man, who Mao allowed to be subjected to terrible adversity in the Cultural Revolution, changed China much more than big, powerful, swaggering Mao. Among other major decisions, Deng had decided that China must have a body of law. The idea that the world's most populous land would exist with no structured legal system was a fact that I found astonishing. My son and I and Jack Downey the lawyer had some interesting conversations about all this.

No less interesting was our visit to the Wu Han University Law School Library, which consisted of no more than seventy-five books, of which the Chinese were immensely proud. On this day, Jack confirmed a relationship between the university and Yale with a letter from the dean of the Yale Law School. To mark this significant event, a grand luncheon was held for us in a cavernous hall. We sat on a raised platform and ate our lengthy lunch with communist cadre officials and leaders of the university. Eating along with us, and staring at us, were hundreds of people in the audience. Speeches were lengthy and effusive. Jack Downey was awarded an honorary doctorate and, reaping the pleasure of an unintended consequence, so was Jack Warner. Mr. Chu was worn out translating, but seemed delighted with the whole affair. He was clearly puffed with his role, and he should have been.

In the course of finishing our luncheon, the Chinese, of course, nagged us into firing down a few maotis. That may have had some influence on a decision that I made when Jack and I were urged to say a few words to the crowd. Jack definitely did not want to speak, and looked at me and asked for a suggestion. I said, "Let's sing them the 'Whiffenpoof Song.'" So Dr. Downey and Dr. Warner stood, with their arms on one another's shoulders, and sang Yale's great song to hundreds of upturned, bewildered Chinese faces.

It had been a long and pleasant day in this waterfront city that had seen some terrible events, both from the Japanese and in the Chinese Civil War. Jack and I were sitting in what passed for the bar in our dingy hotel. As far as night life goes in China, it was late in the evening, perhaps ten o'clock. We were the last patrons left. The room was dimly lit by a single bulb in the corner where a young girl sat, bent over a book, listening to music, and serving cold beer – pijou – from a small refrigerator next to her which constituted the bar's offering. The beer was good as it uniformly was in China. The music was western. The girl had a tape player. Jack commented that such a thing was unheard of in China twenty years ago. "Listening to western music," he said, "would put the listener into prison. Even the homey songs this kid is enjoying." Despite the more than occasional rats that raced up the walls and across the floor, we sat slumped back in our chairs in easy comfort, savoring the warm night, the cold beer, and the moment. The music was quaint and mellow, American songs from long ago, the English words almost forgotten to us: "Old Black Joe," "Jeannie with the Light Brown Hair," and "Home on the Range."

Suddenly the tempo changed and, as we listened, we turned and stared at one another for a moment in wonder. "Jambalaya, crawfish pie, fillet gumbo. Son of a gun, we'll have big fun on the bayou. Good bye Joe, I gotta go, me oh my oh." The song of the B-29 crew from so very long ago. I sat up in my chair, physically and emotionally moved. I was astonished. I had not heard this song played since the mid-1950's. "Have you heard that song since prison, Jack?" I asked.

He shook his head. "No."

I looked closely at him, but he was looking past me, staring at something a long way off.

Our time in Wu Han was over now. It was time for us to go up to Northeast China, to Shenyang, a major city in Manchuria and a focal point for the amazing coincidence that was the Chinese adventure for Jack and Audrey Downey.

Audrey Downey was a graduate student at Yale when Jack

came home from China. She wrote to him, expressing her sympathy, and they met. Audrey Downey was born in Shenyang. Her father, Dr. Li Shotung, head of the local hospital, gathered his family when the Chinese civil war intensified in 1949 and fled to Taiwan.

Jack Downey was brought to Shenyang when he was captured. He spent long, brutal months of interrogation in the cellar of a building somewhere in the city – a building that he came to call "the peanut palace" since that was just about the only food he got.

Leaving our hotel the first morning, we found two old ladies, who are aunts of Audrey's, and a niece, standing timidly outside the hotel parking lot. The old women had been forbidden to enter the area. This was a side of Chinese life that tourists are not aware of. Audrey's relatives are shy and charming. They seem bewildered by the strange twisting of fate that has brought Audrey home with her big American husband. The visit of the Downey family has been a feature of national news in China. The state television had on two occasions run pictures of various officials greeting our party. Despite the paucity of sets, this is said to be a very significant gesture. Chinese newspapers, the English language *China Daily* and, most importantly, *The People's Daily*, the Chinese language newspaper that is the official organ of the government, had carried front page stories of the Downeys' return. A reporter from that newspaper accompanied us to Manchuria. I got a sense that Audrey's relatives up here in the north are a bit afraid of all this. They undoubtedly know too well the historic danger of being too close to the flame of current officialdom in China. I wonder if they know that Audrey has had Jack make a request to the officials to upgrade the housing conditions of her aunts who are aged and ill, forced to live together in one small room.

This morning we are visiting a Chinese school. Mr. Chu tells me that most of the people in this part of Manchuria have seldom, if ever, seen an American. We are told this is Shenyang's most competitive, top-ranked middle school. Fifteen hundred neatly dressed, wide-eyed children from grades six to nine stood at attention on the hard baked exercise field and applauded Jack Downey as he was presented to them as "the spy who has become our friend." It was quite a sight, the fifty-three-year old ex-prisoner returning the applause of the students as he stood on the concrete platform in front of them. The children performed their physical exercise to stirring martial music and then briskly marched into their worn brick school building.

We visited a few classrooms, watched and listened and were very impressed with the intensity of the students. Chris became the center of attention. The Chinese kids seemed fascinated seeing an American contemporary, especially one that is 6'4" tall. Manchuria is not on most tourists' travel plans. We were told that not many Westerners ever visited the school and that, for these young Chinese, Chris was a very rare species. He was asked to read aloud in an English class. The room was completely still with every pupil's eyes concentrated on him. When he finished, they burst into applause; this was not ritualistic, it seemed a spontaneous kind of thing that was very exciting, generated by a real sense of wishing another young person well – a sincere, open, uninhibited "we're glad you're here" kind of feeling that young people the world over often express toward one another, a kind of magic friendliness that sadly seems to be eroded in too many of us during the passage to adulthood.

The next day, our hosts decided to show us some of their history. A little convoy was driven through the car-less countryside to look at the tombs of barely remembered Manchurian emperors. Near mid-day, we spent a rather tedious time being led around the walls of a tomb by two cadre officials who stayed by our side during our time in Manchuria. A combination of the heat of the day and having been pretty well tombed-out by this time caused me to leave our group and head back toward the van. As always in China, there was a steady flow of pedestrians and cyclists. I sat on a rock by the roadside writing some notes.

An old man on what appeared to be an equally old bicycle stopped in front of me and stared at me for a few moments. He watched me closely – I was not uncomfortable; at that time it was an usual occurrence for a Westerner to be stared at in China; it would be especially true in this out-of-the-way place. I glanced at the man. He had short-cropped grey hair and was wearing an under vest, baggy black pajama bottoms knotted at the waist by a rope and the usual black cotton topped hemp slippers. Suddenly and quietly he spoke to me in excellent English.

"Are you American?" he asked.

"Yes," I said, and I expect my face reflected my surprise.

"And are you a writer?"

"I hope so," I answered. He frowned and I spoke quickly. "Yes," I said. "Yes, I am."

His face brightened. "There are seldom Americans here," he said. "Almost never." He continued speaking rapidly and quite clearly. "For many years I have been hoping to meet a writer from America."

A puzzled "Oh" was the best I could do.

"I wish to send a message to my American friends, Mister Yomans and Mister Kane. Can you find them for me with your writing? They live in a place called California."

"I'm afraid I can't be of much help to you," I said. "How do you know them?"

"We were prisoners of the Japanese beginning when America was early in the war," he said. "I am once Korean, now they tell me I am Chinese. Mr. Yoman and Mr. Kanes were kept prisoners with me. They were captured early in the war and brought here to Manchuria. They saved me when I was very sick where we worked in the factory for the Japanese. They helped me through this sickness. Later in the war there was no food and many people starving and friends of mine smuggled food into the prison. I fed Mr. Yoman and Mr. Kane. I was caught and punished and sent to work in a mine. When I was taken away they said they would not forget me and would find me someday. I wish to tell them where I am."

239

I stared at the old man and wished that he had met someone who could do more for him than I knew I could. "I will try," I said.

"I can write English too," he said. "My friends taught me and I still practice. I will write my name and address for you."

address 沈阳市 皇姑区珠江丁三段 10—1号

now name 金岑甲

old name Kaneyama

I have his note here in front of me in the notebook as I write. As he finished writing, he looked around and we both spotted the two cadre officials hurrying toward us. The old man quickly mounted his bicycle and pedalled away.

"Who was that old man?" one of the officials asked me sharply.

"I don't know," I said, closing my notebook.

"What did he want?" His voice was harsh.

"Just practicing his English," I said. "He was asking if I knew a couple of Americans he met during the war."

"He is a liar," the man snarled. And with a heavy frown he looked down the road in the direction the man had headed. I was relieved to see that there was no sight of him in the constant flow of pedestrians, bicycles, horse- and ox-drawn carts and wagons moving along the roadsides. The official reached out his hand towards my notebook, which I put firmly under my arm. In that exchange with this representative of China's government, now standing glaring at my closed notebook, I got a chilling whiff of what Jack Downey's years of subjection in China must have been like.

When we returned to America, I wrote to the Defense

Department and letters to Los Angeles and San Francisco newspapers with a brief summary of this story, asking Mr. Kane or Mr. Yeoman to contact me. When I was in the Marine Corps, I became friendly with a legendary gunner who had been captured at Wake Island. He wore the seldom seen distinctive ribbon with the white W that signified he was part of that moment of Marine Corps glory. He had told me that after their capture the Japs took them to Manchuria where they worked in mines in less than animal conditions. He said some of his comrades starved to death. I wondered if there might be some connection and I wrote to the Marine Corps. I didn't receive any information that I could use. It has always bothered me that I was never able to help.

The day ended in a grey, stone-turreted hotel in the central square of Shanyang. Grey seemed to be the color of the city. Grim and dull and grey. But there was one patch of green here. A circular park in the middle of the square where one of the few remaining statues of Chairman Mao still stood. A massive figure in the heroic mold. A giant striding forward, gathered at his feet are countless bronze men and women carrying weapons, surging along with him toward a happy future.

A banquet was being held in the hotel for us this night by officials of the Friendship Association. On this evening Audrey and Jacky are with relatives. Our group consists of Jack and Chris, six local officials, Mr. Chu, and myself. The warm evening was a very male occasion, with lots of chilled pijou. The food, as always, was delicious. At dinner's end, maotis are poured and re-poured, with toasts and cries of "kom bei" meaning "dry cup" or "down the hatch."

One of the guests was an old Chinese general. Jack and I are sure he must have fought against us in Korea. He is a tough, funny old bird, who enjoys himself enormously.

It was quite a dinner. Despite the language difficulties, there is lots of good conversation about life and families and our hopes for our children and continuing evidence that Chinese and Americans like one another. There is casual, pleasant talk about our two countries, and easy laughter. Dynamite topics like Taiwan are not mentioned. We are strangers yet friends.

Jack Downey had told me that he intentionally refused to speak Chinese in prison. He believed it would signal to his captors that he expected to spend the rest of his life in China. He refused to admit that to the Chinese or himself. Tonight he gave a toast in Chinese and our guests were obviously touched and delighted. Afterward we stood in the gathering dusk in front of the hotel. We were on a small rise where cars pull up to the hotel entrance. It is a vantage point overlooking the city center. Across the way, Mao's figure towered above the endless flow of black-haired cyclists, pumping their way past us around the square. Audrey had come to retrieve us: Jacky was tugging at his father's arm.

Jack turned to me and murmured, "It's a strange life. I was brought here once, to this very spot ...in chains...in a cage...for public interrogation and humiliation."

At that moment I knew why Jack had returned to China. He had won. He wanted the Chinese to know he had won. He was a total man. Free. Happy. He could come and go as he pleased. He was no longer a capitalist running dog kept in chains. He had overcome the Chinese experience. He had become such a man that he did not hate the Chinese or fate. I think Jack Downey was telling the Chinese and the world that he had not just survived, he had prevailed.

# After Words –
# Writer Blocked

My son Chris and I returned to Nantucket and were both rarin'
to get at our goals.  He had lost over ten pounds because of a
savage bout of dysentery which kept him in a small Chinese hospital
for three nights, with me trying to stay awake in a chair by his
bed.  We were monitored by a young, cocky – no – insolent cadre
member with very little English, who alternately glared at the
nervous doctors and nurses and endlessly repeated to me "Chinese
medicine very good."  The experience was unsettling for both
Chris and me.  We were glad to leave China.

Despite his illness and the long trip, Chris was out on the
football practice field with his beloved Nantucket Whalers on the
day he got home.

I was as energized as I have ever been.  I believed I had been
given a writer's opportunity of a lifetime.  I intended to grab my
chance and fulfill my dream of writing one memorable book.  I
was sure the Downey story was that book

Tony Potter, the proud possessor of the highest awards in
television for documentary and news work, was as enthused as I
was.  He believed Jack Downey's saga would fascinate Americans
in print, on television, and he was involved in very promising movie
discussions.

To structure the TV and film part of all this, a company was
formed consisting of Potter, Downey and myself.  It was christened
with a great name that Jack Downey came up with, "JackPot
Productions."  These were exhilarating times for me.

Jack Downey and I spent hours in conversation as he shared
the bitter days and months and years of his purgatory.  We used
the telephone and the Downeys made frequent trips to their

Nantucket house so that Jack and I could have a free and easy exchange of questions, answers. Jack was very giving of his time. His memory was astonishing.

I thought that in the course of his story I would do some flashbacks from his solitary cell to his childhood days in Wallingford and New Britain through his golden years at the Choate School and Yale.

Jack could name the teacher and every student in every seat in every class through the school years. He explained that this was just one of the mental exercises he had practiced during his seventeen years in solitary. He was allowed some books in prison and *encyclopedic* is the word I would use to describe his recall of his reading.

Some people had said to me that twenty-one years in a Chinese prison could be nothing but boring. I found Jack's story riveting. Through his eyes one got an extraordinary look at an intelligent, steadfast young man, bolstered by his religious faith, dealing with a monolithic, cold-blooded state and its savage, dehumanizing doctrine and agents. Despite his circumstances, he was a unique witness to China's wretched turmoil triggered by the mad missteps of Mao.

In 1959, Mao decreed The Great Leap Forward. He ordered that special communes for agriculture and industrialization be organized throughout the vast hive called China. The Party announced that in fifteen years China would outstrip England in the production of major products. This reorganization of the world's most populous nation caused what demographers believe is the most horrendous famine in history.

Some time early in the great famine, someone told Mao that birds ate X amount of China's grain. Mao's solution was swift and terrible.

One day Jack Downey was taken from his cell. He was ordered to bring his metal food bowl. He was led to the roof of the prison which, to his astonishment, was crowded with prisoners and guards. He was given a piece of metal and told to rap it against his bowl. He gazed out from the rooftop across Beijing. There were people everywhere – on rooftops, in trees, on power poles. Everywhere! These people were banging drums, firing weapons (as the guards were doing), banging pots and pans, lighting firecrackers, shouting. This went on day after day, night after night, all across China. One billion people making noise, so that the birds were afraid to settle. They would circle and circle and fall to earth, or alight and immediately be killed.

Mao had decreed that China would kill all the birds. The project was a great success. Insects now devoured the sparse crops that existed.

The accepted number of deaths in this Mao-made starvation is thirty million. Almost as stunning as this number is the fact that the West was essentially unaware that this dreadful nightmare was occurring.

In the prison in Beijing, many of the prisoners died of starvation. For a short time, one of them was a cellmate of Jack Downey.

Mao's reaction to his historic failure was to orchestrate the nation's nervous breakdown which was rightly called a "Cultural Revolution." During this additional grief for the Chinese people, revolutionary factions fought a gun battle for control of Downey's prison. The cold woman ideologue who was Jack's overseer and interpreter was turned into a beast of burden by the revolutionaries. Jack's last view of his former keeper was of her bent almost double as she carried a huge load of filthy bags of charcoal on her back.

Beneath the savage political zigzagging that effected everyone's existence in China, the earthy details of life in a Chinese prison would make you gasp. The sickening realization of where the long worm came from that you watch crawling out of your shit can.

A wise man once told me that he thought that the modern era has been the age of the State against the Family. Jack Downey's story, however, is a pitiless look at the State vs. the Individual. The Chinese had Jack's body; they wanted his mind. They never got it.

Our own government wanted him to be forgotten. His mother, his siblings, friends from Yale, Monsignor Murphy, Senator Dodd and others tried hard to not let that happen.

I tracked down John Woodrow Buck in his little town in Tennessee and spoke with him on the phone. Our conversation was a stunner.

John Woodrow Buck's voice sounded exactly as I thought it would – deep, down-home mountain man. There was a solid quality of goodness that came through the phone to me. I could imagine this man offering to take Jack Downey's place in 1955 when the guards and cadre came and separated him and Richard Fecteau from the Air Force men who were now sure they were going home. This voice would certainly be that of the man who stepped forward to try to save Jack from the fate that the Chinese planned for him. I had identified myself as a friend of Jack Downey's who was writing a book about his experience. Captain Buck asked how Jack was faring. He said he never would forget the day after Christmas when they took Jack out of their dungeon cell. "We knew right off we were goin' home, and he and Fecteau were stayin'. We raised hell – started a riot right there in that dungeon. Smashed up those planks we slept on. The Chinese rushed in a big gang of soldiers. They were all upset. So were we. We knew those boys were headed for an awful time. Two fine young Americans."

John Woodrow Buck's voice began to change. "When we got out of China, the first thing they did with us – they herded us all in a room. There were a couple of generals – one of them three stars – and some civilians, CIA people, of course. One of the civilians did the talking. He read us some law about national security. He threatened us with court martial and prison if we said anything about our experience in China. Said if we were getting out of the military they could come after us if we told anybody – anybody – that we had seen or knew anything about Downey or Fecteau – they'd find out and come after us. We were not to contact their parents, nobody." John Woodrow Buck, that

246

gallant man, was weeping now. "They said we had to forget about those boys or they'd ruin us. I've been ashamed of this ever since. I was a coward. I kept quiet. I never should have. I should have spoken out. I didn't. Nobody ever did. They scared us all and there were some brave men among us. It's the worst thing I've ever done. I've had to live with this all these years. Please tell John Downey how sorry I am. I should have tried to do something."

I filled notebook after notebook. I became consumed by Jack Downey's story. Over three years had passed. I was more than half way through the manuscript of what would be a big book. I had a number of working titles: *Never in Darkness* appealed to me most. I liked the double imagery. Jack physically was never in darkness. The light was on constantly in whatever cell he was in, every minute of every day, all those years. And I believed that spiritually he was also never in darkness.

I did not realize that I was working in darkness.


Tony Potter had some very real movie interest and had talked to a major publisher in New York who wanted to look at the work-in-progress. I sent a copy to the Downeys, a copy to the New York publisher, and a copy to Tony Potter. Things happened then like an avalanche.

A woman editor from the publisher called. She said she had stayed up all night reading the manuscript. She said she was in tears frequently as she read. She advised me that the publisher was prepared to make a sizeable offer for the rights to the book.

Tony Potter called, ecstatic. He felt a movie deal would be forthcoming. He was meeting to show the manuscript to a movie agent who was talking real money for the movie rights.

Audrey Downey called and said the manuscript was unacceptable. She and Jack would not allow it to be published and our relationship was over. She said the story, as I had written it, made it sound as though the Chinese people had treated Jack "like a dog." When the conversation ended, we were both in tears.

Jack Downey called the next day to confirm that he and Audrey did not want the book finished. I suggested I could re-write whatever he found objectionable. He was strangely pleasant to me, seemingly unaware of my anguish. But that was it. The project was over. They were no longer interested in any aspect of JackPot Productions. Jack and I had a handshake deal on all of this, so that was it. Over three years of intense commitment finished, done, evaporated. It left me shaken and hollow.

There was no more communication from our friends the Downeys. In fact, in all the years since, I think I saw Jack at two or three Yale football games. One time I recall an ironic moment up at Harvard. Chris, the little boy who was Jack's companion in China, was playing for Yale. As he and his teammates left the dressing room to go into the stadium for pre-game warm-ups, I was standing in a crowd applauding, and there was Jack Downey standing nearby, clapping. He congratulated me on Chris' achievements and I said "thanks." It was as though we were casual acquaintances. China had never happened. I saw Audrey on the street once in Nantucket. She gave me a "hello" and a warm smile; I said "hi" and walked on.

Even now, after all these years, this is very strange. The whole affair was destructive to my writing ambition. In time I worked on a couple of novels that fell flat. I wrote a biography called *Rebound* of a friend of mine named K.C. Jones who was coach of the NBA champion Boston Celtics, and the book did well. I did another book called *Here's to Nantucket* that was well received. None of this work, however, could take the place of the book that still had the post position in my heart and my head. That book lies half finished on a shelf in my office up in the barn.

It will never be completed.

I've told this part of the story because after years of musing about all this, I decided that this part of Jack Downey's story was also mine.

···

You may recall that I said that when I left Monsignor Murphy he said something to me that haunted me. As he stood at the door, he said, "Mr. Warner, you realize that I never met John Downey." It was a statement that astonished me. Here was a key player in the drama who never met the hero. I'm sure my face showed my surprise. The monsignor and I had spent all our time pursuing my objective, which was to learn as much as I could about Mary Downey's years of struggle to get her son home. Monsignor Murphy had proved eager to talk of the determined lady for whom he clearly had boundless admiration. He was a gold mine of poignant stories of her ceaseless battle for her son. I had assumed that having been Mary Downey's priest, confident, and ally for all those years, he would have met Jack when he came home. The Monsignor continued to speak while I tried to handle his news. "I was transferred from my parish some time before Mr. Downey returned to America. You know, he ran for the United States Senate. When I read that in the paper, I wrote him a letter and reviewed briefly my friendship with his mother. I told him that I was sorry that after all he'd been through he would involve himself in the heartache and turmoil and mess of politics. I said I was writing the letter because I thought that his mother, if she were alive, would feel the same way. In response to my letter I got a very sharp and, I thought insulting, call from Mrs. Downey, followed by a similar letter. I never contacted the Downeys again, nor have I heard from them. Don't put too much hope in this work you're doing, Mr. Warner. I know they asked you to do this, but I would be very much surprised if they will allow a book to be published."

# "As Time Goes By"

*—Music by H. Haupfeld*

# It's Still the Same Old Story

I'm reflecting on events in the year 1986 that changed my life. I'm sure it was '86 because the Patriots played the Bears in the Super Bowl and got whacked. We had a party at 129 Main to watch what quickly became a debacle. That party was memorable for me because of four of the guests that I invited.

As I write this, I wonder if that is the way some historical bellwethers will be marked in future history books. Will some Super Bowl games be added to momentous dates of wars and assassinations or political shifts? If memory serves me, the Greeks and Romans cited certain Olympic or chariot or gladiator events as defining milestones.

I've come to believe there is nothing new in history. We are reliving very old movies; the difference is speed and explosiveness. Man as an historic figure hasn't improved; Super Bowls replace the Coliseum, greed wears different clothes, endless treasure and time are invested in expanding the ways of killing. "Mankind" is one of the grossest misnomers ever concocted.

And yet, it's still the same old story. The dance between men and women in the search for love and companionship continues.

That search for me was complicated. I had been married. I had been a single father on Nantucket for over fifteen years. Now that I know something of the emotional earthquake that cancer brings, I can say that divorce had a similar effect on me. My reaction was visceral. Divorce was a psychological form of cancer for me. I'm sure Freud could give us the definitive phrase. Suffice to say, as I look back, I'm sure that without consciousness of thought I vowed I would never allow myself to be torn apart again by a bad marriage. I knew how to avoid that grief – very simple – don't get married.

It was in 1986 that my subconscious resolution began to be challenged.

For quite a while on my early morning walks downtown, I had noticed some very attractive children waiting for the school bus at the Civil War Monument on Main Street. One night, through an odd coincidence, the divorced mother of three of these children was a guest at my house for dinner with a college teammate of mine who was visiting me. She was there because I had asked a lady friend of mine if she could find a dinner companion for my pal.

This young mother was a striking woman with deep green eyes, dark hair, and flashing spirit. I got the impression that she was full of life and when I realized who she was, I knew her life, in recent years anyway, was very difficult. Her ex-husband's continual harassment of her and its toleration by the police and a strangely unmoved judge were topics of Island comment.

I knew her ex-husband; an unsettled fellow with a well-earned reputation as a bad actor. I learned this woman lived around the corner from me and owned a thriving children's clothing store on South Beach Street. I had never seen those green eyes before.

Her name was Polly.

After waiting for what seemed like a suitable and restrained few days, I called Polly and asked her if she would like to come by for a drink. She said her schedule wouldn't allow that, but that I was welcome to come by her house for a drink before dinner if I could stand the turmoil of her preparing supper and her children and their pals racing around the house.

As I sat in her kitchen and watched the action in her little house on New Dollar Lane, it was soon clear to me that Polly's plate was about as full as a plate could be. Her delightful, boisterous children were her first order of business. Their ages were eight, ten and eleven. Two girls and a boy, each favored with their mother's handsome features. Their vitality was evident from the moment I walked into the kitchen and began uncorking the carefully selected bottle of wine I had brought.

As we chatted, Polly in a kitchen chair, then to the stove, then to the sink, then a dash into the den to check on trampoline exercises on the sofa, this little mother told me about the children's clothing store called "Pinwheels" which she owned and operated.

I was very comfortable with our conversation and I thought Polly was until the loud racing sound of an engine came thundering into the room. New Dollar Lane is just that, a lane. A quiet, short, narrow connector way. There was a small rise in front of Polly's house and someone had roared over that little hillock and raced their engine. Polly stiffened at the sound. "Boy, that's dangerous," I said, "Some kid using the lane as a raceway."

Polly shook her head. "That's no kid, that's my ex-husband."

I stared at her. "This happens a lot?"

She nodded. "A lot. He can see in the kitchen windows driving by. I got tired of living in here with the shades drawn. Now he's seen you sitting in here. I don't know what he'll do."

"How long have you been divorced?"

"Five years."

Her words were almost drowned out by another somehow louder engine roar. "This kind of thing been going on all that time?"

She nodded.

I got up from the table. "Do you mind if I call the cops? This is nuts."

"Don't bother. They won't do anything."

I noticed the children were motionless, staring in on us from the den. Their mother spoke now with a smile that I thought was sad. "Well, thanks for the nice bottle of wine."

I stood with my mind in a muddle. Polly's graceful remark was giving me the option of an exit from an unpleasant situation. I liked her company. I hated bullies. I had ever since I had been a young boy and, with my heart pounding, took on the big tough Polish kid six or seven years older who was in charge of handing out papers to us newspaper boys. I was watching and listening (that roar again) to the worst kind of bullying. A man oppressing a woman. And it certainly must be effecting these children. What should my role be? I hardly knew this beleaguered band, but we all recognize evil when we see it – or hear it. Strolling around the corner to home wasn't an option.

Did I see this as a moment when the hinge of fate of my future was about to swing and open a new chapter of my life? No. I had drifted into some nasty business that needed attention. I knew the man who was doing this. He knew me. I decided to see if he might be embarrassed to have another man observe his behavior. Without any words being spoken, I went out the front door and stood on the sidewalk in front of the house. He came by again, didn't race and roar, glared at me, and didn't come back. This was to prove just like winning on the first horse you bet on the first time you go to the racetrack. It was to be the only time he ever evinced any embarrassment in his behavior.

I went back in the house, we finished the bottle of wine. When I left, Polly was setting the table and one of the kids was bouncing on the sofa.

Although I was not conscious of the scripting, a new scene had begun. The movie was being recast. I called again a day or two later and went around the corner with another bottle of wine.

It seemed that we had found a comfort zone in sharing the pleasure of a glass of wine and the conversation one hopes will accompany it. In a short time, that comfort zone expanded. We began to go out to dinner. There is no more public announcement of emotional interest on Nantucket than an unattached male and female going out to dinner. My longtime right hand secretary/housekeeper/pal, Beth Hanlon, helped make this possible by allowing herself to be drafted into the babysitting ranks at New Dollar Lane.

The ex-husband's wicked behavior escalated as my relationship with Polly grew.

Polly and her children were among the guests at the Super Bowl party at 129 Main Street. I remember giving Polly a quick kiss – or trying to – when we were in the kitchen area between the wood-burning stove and the sink, and looking down and seeing her angelic daughter Amy staring wide-eyed at the pair of us. That was a defining moment.

So, after seeking – or avoiding – a perfect partner in various ports of call for all those years, I seemed to have found her around the corner. You know how it is sometimes when you meet someone and are struck by what you perceive to be their exceptional, perhaps unique, qualities? Then, as time passes, one sees flaws or weaknesses – perhaps major, hopefully not. I don't think I am an advocate of the familiarity breeds contempt school, but the phrase hasn't echoed down the canyons of time by accident. I'm sure the theme has been tested intensely in man's search for a partner. As I got to know Polly, I found the obverse side of that philosophy. And it brought a wonderful, sunny glow of well-being to me. Simply put, the more time I spent with her, the more certain I was that Polly was a splendid person. She seemed to deal with life as it came. Despite the turmoil that buffeted her, she never ever complained. She was an upbeat, winsome lady. Did I say she made no demands on me?

In fact, as our relationship deepened, and my pleasure in her company was confirmed, she never mentioned marriage, which I'm sure had something to do with the sunshine of contentment that warmed me. Most ladies I had known for an extended period of time got to the subject of marriage sooner or sooner. It never increased my ardor.

A happy year passed. As far as I knew, the thought of marriage never crossed Polly's mind, until one day when she spoke very simply and quietly to me. "Jack, I realize that you have no intention of getting married again, and I can understand why – you've raised your kids – you're in a very comfortable position here on the Island. The last thing you need is a woman with three small children and a lunatic ex-husband."

I'm not sure what my answer was, but I am sure I didn't disagree or deny. In fact, two good pals of mine had separately conducted heart-to-heart talks with me saying how much they liked Polly... "but three little kids, a bizarre, troublesome ex-husband, that's a lot of baggage to take on." I kept my own counsel on these things.

Polly continued speaking in the same thoughtful tone. "We've had wonderful times together, but I have got to move on. I can't expect you to take on the kids and the burden of dealing with the wild man. I've got to get myself and the children away. You know I own some land in Idaho. I love it out there. I've rented a house in Ketchum. I've talked with Beth and she's willing to help me move and to run the shop. I want to do this as quietly as possible. I plan to leave next week so the kids can be there for the start of school."

That was that; no tears or drama; no pleading or ranting; a simple, logical well reasoned giant step to restart her life.

I was stunned. A mix of emotions percolated in me.

I was going to miss her. Already the sunshine had dimmed. At the same time, I was full of admiration for her. In leaving and in the way she was leaving, she was proving to be the gutsy, independent person I thought she was. Mixed in with my sadness, I was proud of her.

Nantucket empties right after Labor Day. People, cars, noise, attitude are all diminished. This lessening continues until winter when you become more aware of where you are, and a special stillness settles on the island.

Polly and her children left a few days before Labor Day. In the days and weeks that followed, a wintry stillness came upon me. We spoke on the phone from time to time, and on one occasion she revealed that early in the morning on their first day in Idaho, she heard a noise on the porch. She got up and looked out and was stunned to see her ex-husband standing there. He let her know that wherever she went he would follow her.

One day I suggested that I would like to visit Idaho. My suggestion was accepted. I made my travel plans. I thought my trip to Idaho would be memorable, and perhaps to reinforce that, I decided to take the train. I had always had a deep hankering to ride a train across America.  Here was a chance to come close to fulfilling my dream.

With a plan made, I called Polly.  The transcontinental train from Boston would drop me off in a little town in Idaho named after the Indian tribe, Shoshone.  The word thrilled me.  I was going to see some of the west that I had dreamed of as a kid, and also see the woman I had been dreaming of now.

When I boarded the train in Boston, I think I knew that the step from the concrete platform onto the train was a very big one.

I settled into my compartment with a couple of good books and a six-pack – heading west!  How good was that?

As the train slid out of the station, a sprightly, smiling black man of indeterminant age dressed in a shiny, spotless, navy blue uniform stood in the open door of my cozy little suite and announced that he was my attendant.  His name, as I recall, was Everett.  He said he would be with me all the way across the country.  I think we liked one another on sight.  I offered him a beer which he politely refused.  Everett never did have a beer with me, but he often sat and chatted and watched me drink a number of them as we racketed along the ever changing features of America.  Boston to Albany took me through western Massachusetts where I grew up, and I looked for landmarks and saw place names that I had known forever.  I figure the preceding years of one's life, leading up to the present moment, are forever. You may well ask, if the past is forever, what is the future called? I guess, the unknown will suffice.  I was very aware that I was looking towards the unknown as the train headed west.

I still remember the shock as we rumbled along upper New York State through Buffalo into Pennsylvania and Ohio along Lake Erie.  Places like Toledo and Cleveland that to me had signified the industrial muscle of America, showed mile after mile of flab. A depressing, seemingly non-stop view of decaying, rusting, blighted factories whose broken windows seemed to symbolize shattered dreams and lives.  Trains generally traverse America's backyards, and America's backyards were telling me a woeful story that I hadn't heard. Our country's almost mythical industrial heartland had suffered what looked to me to be a fatal heart attack, and no one had written the obituary. If they had, most of the rest of America hadn't read it. There had been no funerals or elegies, only abandonment.

When I was a kid, Chicago was the most popular town in America for World War II veterans. Their praise had stayed with me through the years. Fellows older than I would reminisce and look into their drink with a fond look in their eyes. "During the war," they would say, "a guy in uniform never had to pay for a drink in Chicago."

Chicago was the big stop on my transcontinental trip. Here we changed trains and I learned that the bridge heights to the west were built tall enough to accommodate observation cars – cars with an upper story where you could sit in glassed-in comfort and watch us race past the world outside. From Chicago west, the world became a very different place – another America, the one I had longed to see, the place of the prairies and the mountains, of cowboys and fur trappers, the place where the deer and the antelope play. I watched them with delight, and believe me, there seldom was heard a discouraging word in my observation car.

I am an obsessive reader. Television for me is generally something I look up from a book and glance at. Not so with my last full day in the observation car. The view was my book. The pages turned swiftly as we raced across a landscape that held me riveted and never disappointed me. Strange, I had been to some of the world's legendary places. I had been around the world, but nothing had pleased me as this train ride across America the beautiful.

That night I packed for a 4:00 a.m. arrival in Shoshone. Everett came in and we talked about the country that we both loved. He lived in New Orleans. He had worked on the railroad for almost thirty years. He loved his job. He said he and his wife had put their three kids through college. Told me he didn't drink, but if he did, he would enjoy having one with me.

I don't think I slept much that night. I had become not only accustomed, but comforted by the rapid, now almost imperceptible, click click of the wheels on the rails. The sound became a memory. I was a little boy, cozy in my bed, my brother snoring beside me. The sound of rain on the tin roof became the patter on my poncho as I curled up on the prairie near my fire. My ten-gallon hat covered my face. My beloved horse, Pal, cropped at the grass nearby. My long-barrel Colt was out of its holster and close to my hand. Lightening Jack, the fastest gun in the west, was bedded down for the night, warm, dry and ready, despite the driving rain.

I was dressed and set to go when Everett tapped on my door around 3:45. We were coming up on Shoshone. He opened the exit door and we stood unspeaking, staring out at the dark. I looked back and admired the long silver train that shone in the black landscape. I looked up at one of the biggest, starriest skies I had ever seen.

The train began to slow – a few scraggly houses, low, wooden-framed shops appeared. This superb transcontinental hotel on wheels was slowly moving down the middle of the main street of Shoshone, Idaho. Everett looked at me and spoke. "The train won't stop, you'll have to toss off your bag and get off while we move along." He glanced now at the weather-beaten, seemingly abandoned fragile looking wooden structures caught in the train's light along the street. "You sure you want to get off here, Mr. Warner?" The train was moving very slowly now. I tossed my bag off.

"I'm sure, Everett. Good luck."

"Good luck to you, sir," he said as I carefully swung down from the train and took some half running steps to steady myself.

The sinuous, silver, iron horse picked up its pace quickly, and I watched the tail disappear into the night. I stood in the darkness of Shoshone. There were no street lights. There was a cold, dusty wind blowing. There was not a person in sight.

A sound of banging caught my attention as I retrieved my bag. I turned toward this uneasy noise and saw a two-story wooden building with a porch and an outside stairway leading to the second floor. The faded sign over the porch announced "The Boston Hotel." Behind the dust-streaked window of the front door, I could make out a For Sale sign. The windows of the place looked like dead men's eyes. The sound I was hearing was the Hotel Boston's remaining shutters slapping against the tired old building – much too late to get its attention.

I hefted my bag and climbed up onto the wood-plank sidewalk. I was looking for the railroad station where Polly and I had planned to meet. Not far along, a dim light caught my eye. The sidewalk broadened into a wide platform that fronted a low-peaked building that, as I got closer, seemed to be constructed of adobe brick. A sign hanging over the wide door announced "Shoshone Station." I tried the door. It was locked solid. I went around to where the light showed through the window. I think I held my breath when I looked in. A man was seated with his booted feet up on the writing surface of a roll-top desk. He was wearing a green-visored eyeshade. The sleeves of his white shirt were pulled up by elastics on his upper arms. There was a long tubed black telephone with its earpiece hanging ready at hand. On a nearby table I recognized a telegraph set. A pot-bellied stove sat in the center of the room. The man stirred in his chair. He was fast asleep. To use a long-gone phrase, I almost hugged myself with delight as I stared at the scene.

Finally, regretfully, I tapped on the window, waited a bit, then rapped hard. The man's feet came down and he sprang from his chair. His glance came to my window and I thought I could see fear on his face. "What do you want?" he shouted.

"Can I leave a suitcase in there?"

"You can't come in here. We're not open til later. Leave the bag on the dolly."

"Was there a woman waiting here?"

"No." He sat down and put his feet back up.

For a moment there, I felt like Jesse James. Now I picked up my bag and went around to the street front. Still no one in sight.

Polly and I were not on the same page here. I couldn't imagine spending too many days in Shoshone, especially with the Boston Hotel closed. As I was standing there, a neon sign came on far down the street on the other side of the tracks. I fished paper and pen from my jacket and wrote a note to Polly telling her, among other things, that I would be at the neon sign. I fixed the note onto the top of the bag and headed toward the blinking red sign. The wind was kicking up little dust swirls along the track.

As I got closer to the sign, the letters became clear: New York Cafe. No doubt about it, Shoshone was a cosmopolitan town.

There were three or four dirt-streaked pickup trucks in front of the cafe when I got there. Four or five fellows, cowboy hats, jeans, and boots, were silently having breakfast. The lady behind the counter sure looked like an Indian. I wondered if she was a Shoshone. No one was speaking. I could feel everyone's eyes on me. I ordered a cup of tea and sipped it slowly, thinking about Polly, wondering what life might have up its sleeve for me that day.

Polly came in the door. We realized the time zones had confused us on our meeting.

The sun was rising as we headed out of Shoshone. It was the beginning of a new day and a new life for both of us.